ONE-MINUTE PUZZLES

Capella

This edition published in 2014 by Arcturus Publishing Limited
26/27 Bickels Yard, 151–153 Bermondsey Street,
London SE1 3HA

ISBN: 978-1-84837-365-5
AD001181NT

Printed in the UK by Clays Ltd, St Ives plc

CONTENTS

INTRODUCTION

Life is so fast-paced that we need to make sure our brains are in good enough shape to keep up. The challenges presented in *One-Minute Puzzles* have been specially devised to accelerate your mental processes so that you are never stuck for the right answer.

We have chosen five very effective puzzle types for your workout: number crunch, one to nine, pyramid plus, summing up and isolate. Each of these can be solved quickly by experienced puzzlers, most of them within the 60-second target time.

But don't worry if you are off the pace to begin with – your times will improve as your brain gets used to what is demanded.

Once you get in the groove, you will lose your inhibitions and positively relish the challenge of *One-Minute Puzzles*.

How Quick Are YOU?

Record your start and finish times in the panels provided, to monitor your progress. Once you understand the solving process you should notice that it takes you less time to complete a particular type of puzzle.

One to Nine

Using the numbers below, complete these six equations
(three reading across and three reading downwards).
Every number is used once.

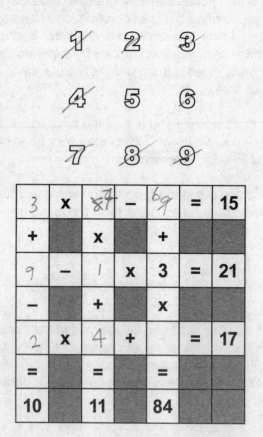

3	x	8̷7̸	–	6̸9̸	=	15
+		x		+		
9	–	1	x	3	=	21
–		+		x		
2	x	4	+		=	17
=		=		=		
10		11		84		

2

Number Crunch

Starting at the left with the number provided, work across from one box to another, applying the mathematical instructions to your running total.

Beginner							Answer
94	− 16	÷ 2	2/3 of this	+ 14	3/5 of this	× 3	+ 28	

Intermediate							Answer
2222	÷ 11	150% of this	+ 30	5/37 of this	÷ 15	2/3 of this	× 86	

Advanced							Answer
247	3/13 of this	5/19 of this	× 35	5/21 of this	Cube root of this	× 1.4	× 45	

Summing Up

Arrange one of each of the four given numbers, as well as one each of the symbols – (minus), x (times) and + (plus) in every row and column to arrive at the answer at the end of the row or column, making the calculations in the order in which they appear.

3	+	8	x	2	–	7	=	15
						+		
						=	48	
		+						
						=	24	
		2				=	12	
=		=		=		=		
64		8		33		27		

8

Isolate

Draw walls to partition the grid into areas (some walls are already drawn in for you). Each area must contain two circles, area sizes must match those shown by the numbers next to the grid and each '+' must be linked to at least two walls.

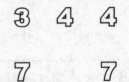

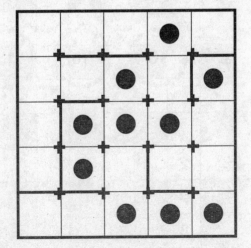

Pyramid Plus

The number in each circle is the sum of the two numbers below it. Just work out the missing numbers in every circle!

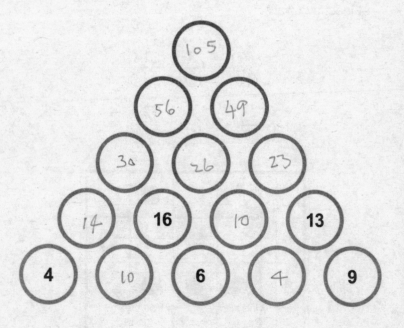

105

56   49

30   26   23

14   **16**   10   **13**

4   10   **6**   4   **9**

6

One to Nine

Using the numbers below, complete these six equations
(three reading across and three reading downwards).
Every number is used once.

	–		x		=	35
+		+		x		
	x		+		=	21
–		x		+		
	x		–	7	=	17
=		=		=		
6		60		22		

Number Crunch

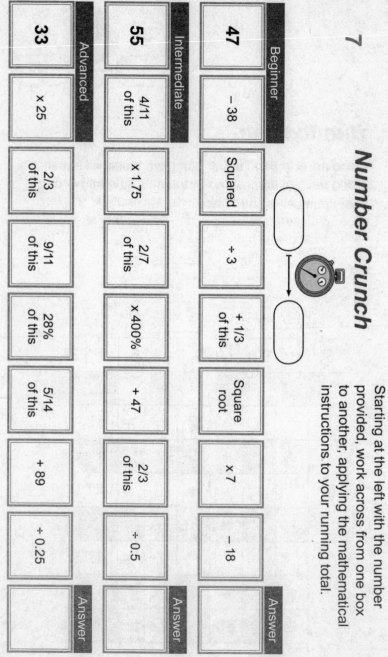

Starting at the left with the number provided, work across from one box to another, applying the mathematical instructions to your running total.

Beginner

| 47 | − 38 | Squared | ÷ 3 | + 1/3 of this | Square root | × 7 | − 18 | Answer |

Intermediate

| 55 | 4/11 of this | × 1.75 | 2/7 of this | × 400% | + 47 | 2/3 of this | ÷ 0.5 | Answer |

Advanced

| 33 | × 25 | 2/3 of this | 9/11 of this | 28% of this | 5/14 of this | + 89 | ÷ 0.25 | Answer |

Summing Up

Arrange one of each of the four given numbers, as well as one each of the symbols – (minus), x (times) and + (plus) in every row and column to arrive at the answer at the end of the row or column, making the calculations in the order in which they appear.

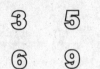

5	+	9	x	3	–	6	=	36
	x			6			=	18
9							=	72
							=	32
=		=		=		=		
24		42		14		40		

Isolate

Draw walls to partition the grid into areas (some walls are already drawn in for you). Each area must contain two circles, area sizes must match those shown by the numbers next to the grid and each '+' must be linked to at least two walls.

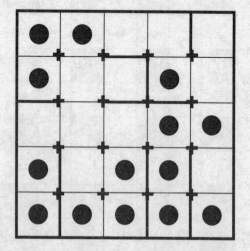

Pyramid Plus

The number in each circle is the sum of the two numbers below it. Just work out the missing numbers in every circle!

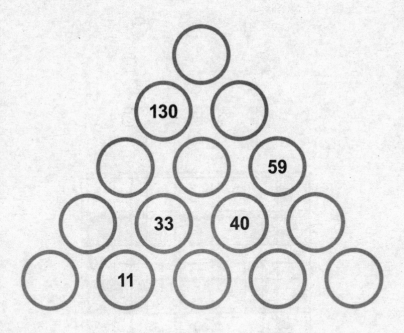

One to Nine

Using the numbers below, complete these six equations (three reading across and three reading downwards). Every number is used once.

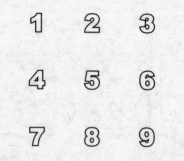

1   2   3

4   5   6

7   8   9

	+		−		=	4
+		−		x		
	x		−		=	10
x		+		−		
	−	1	x		=	32
=		=		=		
72		5		36		

Number Crunch

12

Starting at the left with the number provided, work across from one box to another, applying the mathematical instructions to your running total.

Beginner

6	1/3 of this	Squared	× 8	3/8 of this	+ 98	10% of this	× 12	Answer

Intermediate

59	× 3	− 114	+ 1/3 of this	5/12 of this	3/7 of this	× 13	+ 85	Answer

Advanced

578	÷ 2	Square root	+ 68	80% of this	× 1.75	Double it	− 109	Answer

Summing Up

Arrange one of each of the four given numbers, as well as one each of the symbols – (minus), x (times) and + (plus) in every row and column to arrive at the answer at the end of the row or column, making the calculations in the order in which they appear.

6	x	9	–	4	+	7	=	57
		7					=	12
				6			=	27
							=	32
=		=		=		=		
23		72		37		13		

Isolate

Draw walls to partition the grid into areas (some walls are already drawn in for you). Each area must contain two circles, area sizes must match those shown by the numbers next to the grid and each '+' must be linked to at least two walls.

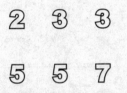

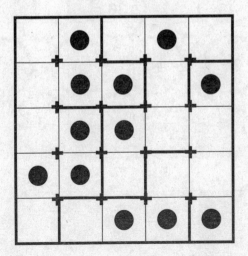

Pyramid Plus

The number in each circle is the sum of the two numbers below it. Just work out the missing numbers in every circle!

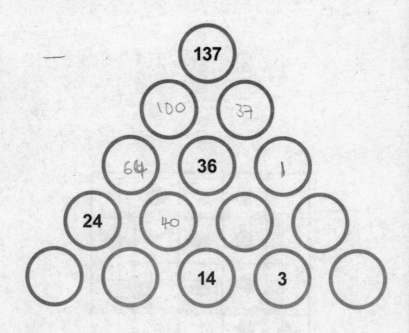

One to Nine

Using the numbers below, complete these six equations (three reading across and three reading downwards). Every number is used once.

1 2 3

4 5 6

7 8 9

	+	4	x		=	63
−		x		+		
	x		−		=	26
x		+		x		
	x		+		=	20
=		=		=		
4		42		64		

Number Crunch

Starting at the left with the number provided, work across from one box to another, applying the mathematical instructions to your running total.

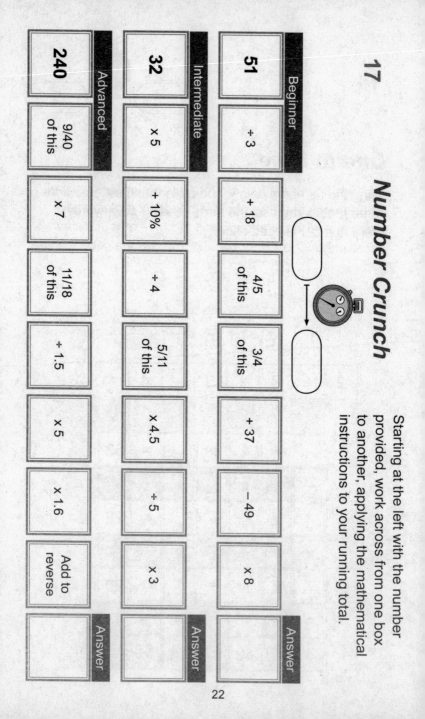

Beginner

| 51 | ÷ 3 | + 18 | 4/5 of this | 3/4 of this | + 37 | − 49 | × 8 | Answer |

Intermediate

| 32 | × 5 | + 10% | ÷ 4 | 5/11 of this | × 4.5 | ÷ 5 | × 3 | Answer |

Advanced

| 240 | 9/40 of this | × 7 | 11/18 of this | ÷ 1.5 | × 5 | × 1.6 | Add to reverse | Answer |

Summing Up

Arrange one of each of the four given numbers, as well as one each of the symbols – (minus), x (times) and + (plus) in every row and column to arrive at the answer at the end of the row or column, making the calculations in the order in which they appear.

2	+	8	x	5	–	4	=	46
							=	26
4							=	43
		x						
							=	42
=		=		=		=		
14		30		28		58		

Isolate

Draw walls to partition the grid into areas (some walls are already drawn in for you). Each area must contain two circles, area sizes must match those shown by the numbers next to the grid and each '+' must be linked to at least two walls.

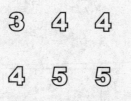

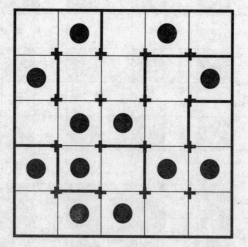

Pyramid Plus

The number in each circle is the sum of the two numbers below it. Just work out the missing numbers in every circle!

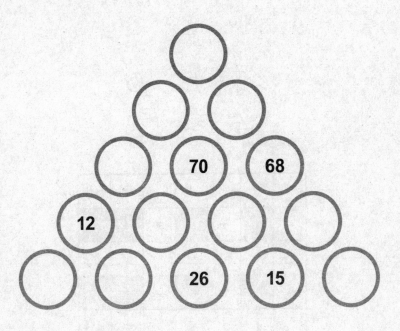

One to Nine

Using the numbers below, complete these six equations (three reading across and three reading downwards). Every number is used once.

	x		+		=	30
−		+		x		
5	+		x		=	49
+		x		−		
	+		x		=	40
=		=		=		
4		45		38		

Number Crunch

Starting at the left with the number provided, work across from one box to another, applying the mathematical instructions to your running total.

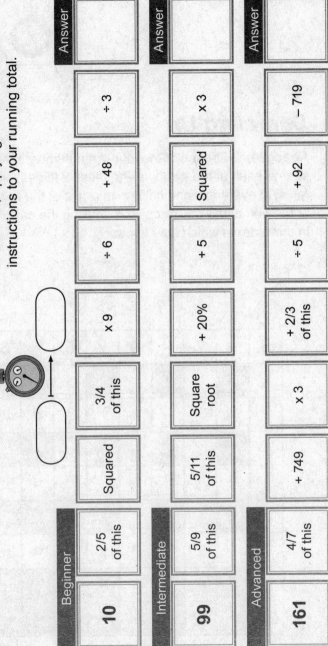

Beginner

| 10 | 2/5 of this | Squared | 3/4 of this | × 9 | ÷ 6 | + 48 | ÷ 3 | **Answer** |

Intermediate

| 99 | 5/9 of this | 5/11 of this | Square root | + 20% | + 5 | Squared | × 3 | **Answer** |

Advanced

| 161 | 4/7 of this | + 749 | × 3 | + 2/3 of this | ÷ 5 | + 92 | − 719 | **Answer** |

23

Summing Up

Arrange one of each of the four given numbers, as well as one each of the symbols – (minus), x (times) and + (plus) in every row and column to arrive at the answer at the end of the row or column, making the calculations in the order in which they appear.

3	+	7	–	9	x	6	=	6
x								
							=	43
				–				
							=	58
7				3	x		=	36
=		=		=		=		
26		42		24		48		

Isolate

Draw walls to partition the grid into areas (some walls are already drawn in for you). Each area must contain two circles, area sizes must match those shown by the numbers next to the grid and each '+' must be linked to at least two walls.

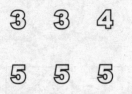

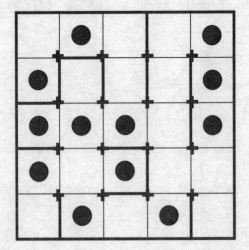

Pyramid Plus

The number in each circle is the sum of the two numbers below it. Just work out the missing numbers in every circle!

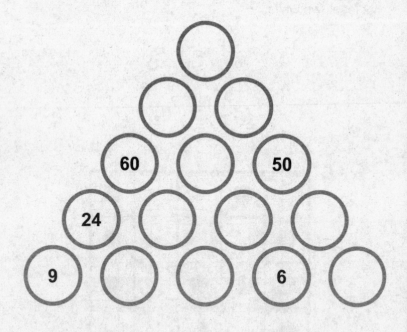

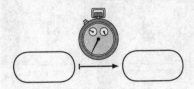

One to Nine

Using the numbers below, complete these six equations
(three reading across and three reading downwards).
Every number is used once.

	+	2	x		=	30
+		x		−		
	+		−		=	12
−		+		x		
	−		x		=	49
=		=		=		
2		19		14		

31

Number Crunch

Starting at the left with the number provided, work across from one box to another, applying the mathematical instructions to your running total.

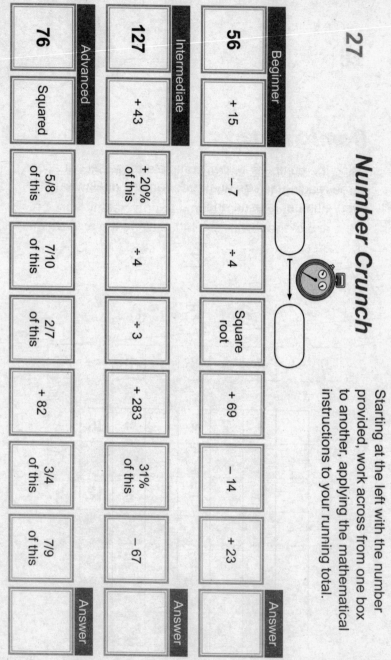

Beginner

| 56 | + 15 | − 7 | ÷ 4 | Square root | + 69 | − 14 | + 23 | Answer |

Intermediate

| 127 | + 43 | + 20% of this | ÷ 4 | ÷ 3 | + 283 | 31% of this | − 67 | Answer |

Advanced

| 76 | Squared | 5/8 of this | 7/10 of this | 2/7 of this | + 82 | 3/4 of this | 7/9 of this | Answer |

Summing Up

Arrange one of each of the four given numbers, as well as one each of the symbols – (minus), x (times) and + (plus) in every row and column to arrive at the answer at the end of the row or column, making the calculations in the order in which they appear.

6	+	4	x	8	–	3	=	77
						=	26	
x								
	–			+		=	14	
		3			=	44		
=		=		=		=		
20		30		27		22		

Isolate

Draw walls to partition the grid into areas (some walls are already drawn in for you). Each area must contain two circles, area sizes must match those shown by the numbers next to the grid and each '+' must be linked to at least two walls.

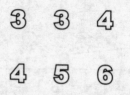

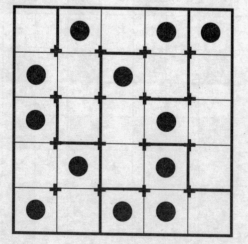

Pyramid Plus

The number in each circle is the sum of the two numbers below it. Just work out the missing numbers in every circle!

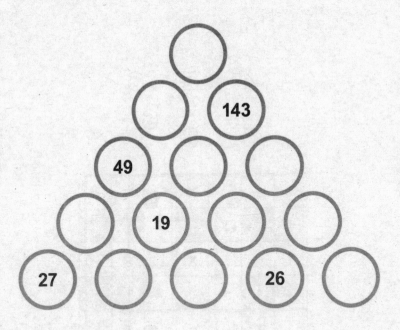

One to Nine

Using the numbers below, complete these six equations (three reading across and three reading downwards). Every number is used once.

	–		x		=	8
+		x		+		
1	+		x		=	36
x		+		x		
	x		–		=	33
=		=		=		
45		25		26		

36

Number Crunch

Starting at the left with the number provided, work across from one box to another, applying the mathematical instructions to your running total.

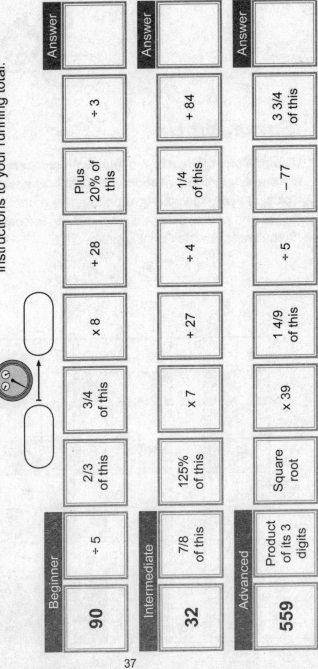

Beginner							Answer
90	÷ 5	2/3 of this	3/4 of this		× 8	+ 28	Plus 20% of this	÷ 3	

Intermediate							Answer
32	7/8 of this	125% of this	× 7	+ 27	÷ 4	1/4 of this	+ 84	

Advanced							Answer
559	Product of its 3 digits	Square root	× 39	1 4/9 of this	÷ 5	– 77	3 3/4 of this	

32

Summing Up

Arrange one of each of the four given numbers, as well as one each of the symbols – (minus), x (times) and + (plus) in every row and column to arrive at the answer at the end of the row or column, making the calculations in the order in which they appear.

2 5

7 9

5	+	9	x	2	–	7	=	21
							=	12
				9			=	50
					x		=	22
=		=		=		=		
90		15		76		78		

Isolate

Draw walls to partition the grid into areas (some walls are already drawn in for you). Each area must contain two circles, area sizes must match those shown by the numbers next to the grid and each '+' must be linked to at least two walls.

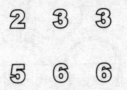

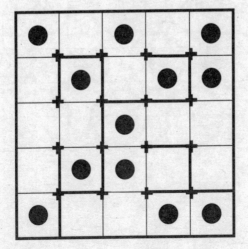

Pyramid Plus

The number in each circle is the sum of the two numbers below it. Just work out the missing numbers in every circle!

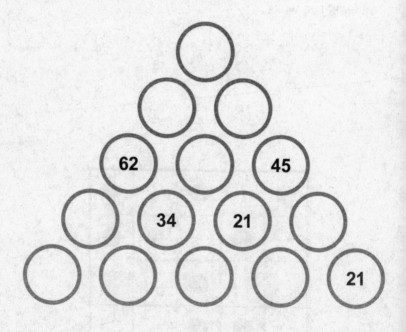

One to Nine

Using the numbers below, complete these six equations
(three reading across and three reading downwards).
Every number is used once.

	−	3	x		=	48
+		x		−		
	+		x		=	40
x		−		x		
	+		−		=	10
=		=		=		
77		14		3		

41

Number Crunch

Starting at the left with the number provided, work across from one box to another, applying the mathematical instructions to your running total.

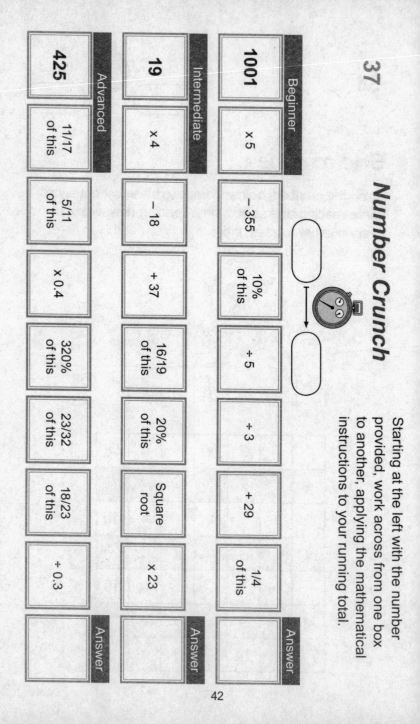

Beginner

| 1001 | × 5 | 10% of this | ÷ 5 | ÷ 3 | + 29 | 1/4 of this | Answer |

Intermediate

| 19 | × 4 | − 18 | + 37 | 16/19 of this | 20% of this | Square root | × 23 | Answer |

Advanced

| 425 | 11/17 of this | 5/11 of this | × 0.4 | 320% of this | 23/32 of this | 18/23 of this | ÷ 0.3 | Answer |

Summing Up

Arrange one of each of the four given numbers, as well
as one each of the symbols – (minus), x (times) and +
(plus) in every row and column to arrive at the answer
at the end of the row or column, making the calculations
in the order in which they appear.

3 4

7 8

4	+	7	x	3	–	8	=	25
				7			=	39
	x				+		=	11
			+				=	57
=		=		=		=		
36		24		76		33		

43

Isolate

Draw walls to partition the grid into areas (some walls are already drawn in for you). Each area must contain two circles, area sizes must match those shown by the numbers next to the grid and each '+' must be linked to at least two walls.

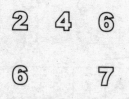

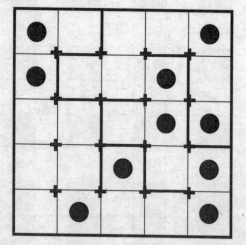

Pyramid Plus

The number in each circle is the sum of the two numbers below it. Just work out the missing numbers in every circle!

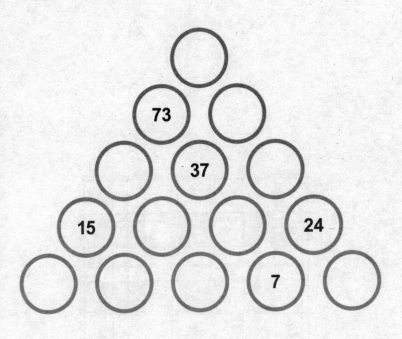

One to Nine

Using the numbers below, complete these six equations (three reading across and three reading downwards). Every number is used once.

1 2 3

4 5 6

7 8 9

	+		x		=	35
x		+		–		
	+		–		=	12
–		x		+		
3	x		+		=	24
=		=		=		
21		45		14		

Number Crunch

Starting at the left with the number provided, work across from one box to another, applying the mathematical instructions to your running total.

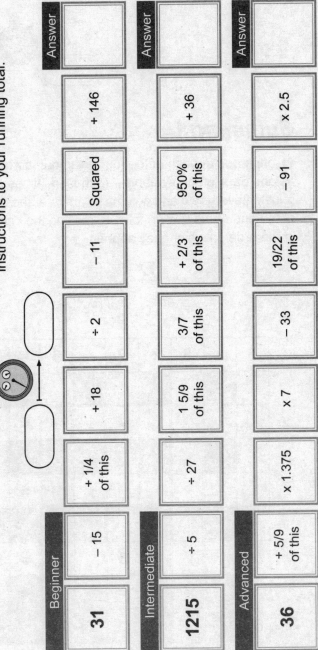

Beginner

| 31 | − 15 | + 1/4 of this | + 18 | ÷ 2 | − 11 | Squared | + 146 | Answer |

Intermediate

| 1215 | ÷ 5 | ÷ 27 | 1 5/9 of this | 3/7 of this | + 2/3 of this | 950% of this | + 36 | Answer |

Advanced

| 36 | + 5/9 of this | x 1.375 | x 7 | − 33 | 19/22 of this | − 91 | x 2.5 | Answer |

Summing Up

Arrange one of each of the four given numbers, as well as one each of the symbols – (minus), x (times) and + (plus) in every row and column to arrive at the answer at the end of the row or column, making the calculations in the order in which they appear.

5	x	8	+	2	–	6	=	36
							=	28
	–				x		=	18
						–		
				8			=	59
=		=		=		=		
86		66		12		23		

Isolate

Draw walls to partition the grid into areas (some walls are already drawn in for you). Each area must contain two circles, area sizes must match those shown by the numbers next to the grid and each '+' must be linked to at least two walls.

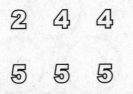

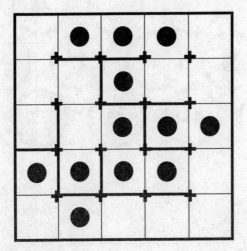

Pyramid Plus

The number in each circle is the sum of the two numbers below it. Just work out the missing numbers in every circle!

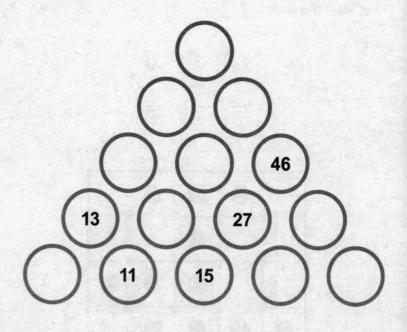

One to Nine

Using the numbers below, complete these six equations (three reading across and three reading downwards). Every number is used once.

1   2   3

4   5   6

7   8   9

	x		−	9	=	9
+		−		+		
	+		x		=	49
x		x		x		
	−		+		=	11
=		=		=		
40		1		64		

Number Crunch

Starting at the left with the number provided, work across from one box to another, applying the mathematical instructions to your running total.

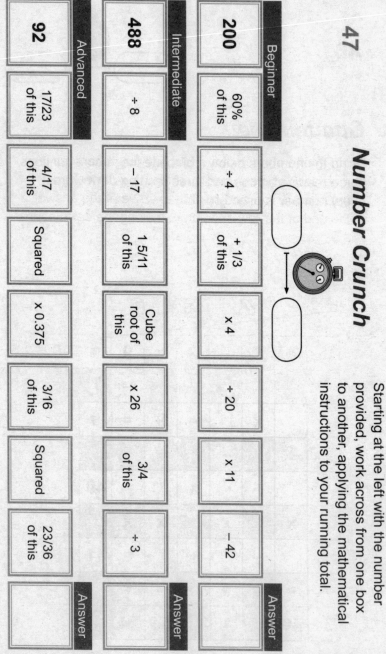

Beginner

| 200 | 60% of this | ÷ 4 | + 1/3 of this | x 4 | ÷ 20 | x 11 | − 42 | Answer |

Intermediate

| 488 | ÷ 8 | − 17 | 1 5/11 of this | Cube root of this | x 26 | 3/4 of this | ÷ 3 | Answer |

Advanced

| 92 | 17/23 of this | 4/17 of this | Squared | x 0.375 | 3/16 of this | Squared | 23/36 of this | Answer |

Summing Up

Arrange one of each of the four given numbers, as well as one each of the symbols – (minus), x (times) and + (plus) in every row and column to arrive at the answer at the end of the row or column, making the calculations in the order in which they appear.

5	+	7	–	2	x	9	=	90
						–		
						=	12	
				7	+		=	54
						x		
						=	78	
=		=		=		=		
34		15		16		14		

Isolate

Draw walls to partition the grid into areas (some walls are already drawn in for you). Each area must contain two circles, area sizes must match those shown by the numbers next to the grid and each '+' must be linked to at least two walls.

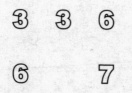

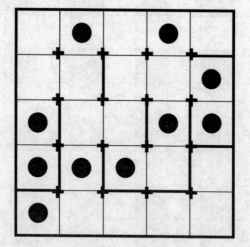

Pyramid Plus

The number in each circle is the sum of the two numbers below it. Just work out the missing numbers in every circle!

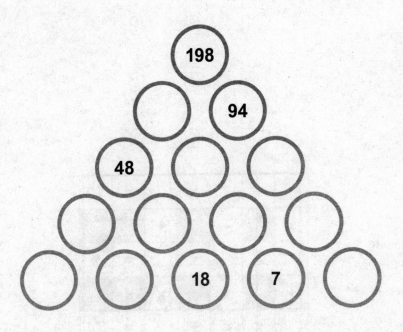

One to Nine

Using the numbers below, complete these six equations (three reading across and three reading downwards). Every number is used once.

1   2   3

4   5   6

7   8   9

	+		x		=	10
x		−		+		
	−		x		=	9
+		x		x		
	x	4	+		=	34
=		=		=		
26		8		20		

Number Crunch

Starting at the left with the number provided, work across from one box to another, applying the mathematical instructions to your running total.

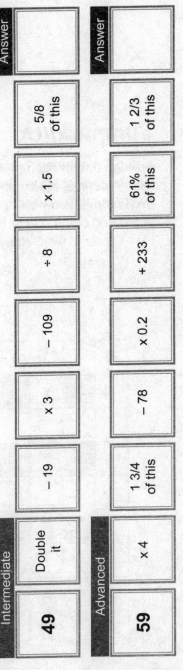

Beginner								Answer
95	+ 18	− 72	x 2	1.5 times this	− 16	− 17	x 4	

Intermediate								Answer
49	Double it	− 19	x 3	− 109	÷ 8	x 1.5	5/8 of this	

Advanced								Answer
59	x 4	1 3/4 of this	− 78	x 0.2	+ 233	61% of this	1 2/3 of this	

Summing Up

Arrange one of each of the four given numbers, as well as one each of the symbols − (minus), x (times) and + (plus) in every row and column to arrive at the answer at the end of the row or column, making the calculations in the order in which they appear.

5	−	3	+	8	x	7	=	70
		x						
							=	30
							=	26
	−		x				=	14
=		=		=		=		
32		18		24		40		

Isolate

Draw walls to partition the grid into areas (some walls are already drawn in for you). Each area must contain two circles, area sizes must match those shown by the numbers next to the grid and each '+' must be linked to at least two walls.

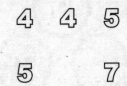

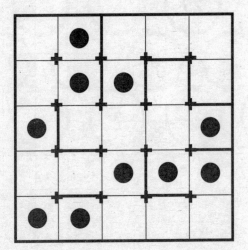

Pyramid Plus

The number in each circle is the sum of the two numbers below it. Just work out the missing numbers in every circle!

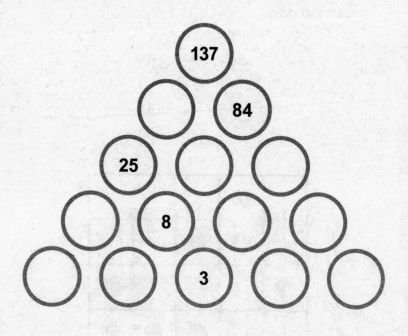

One to Nine

Using the numbers below, complete these six equations
(three reading across and three reading downwards).
Every number is used once.

	x		−		=	30
x		+		−		
3	+		x		=	10
+		−		+		
	−		x		=	6
=		=		=		
20		11		7		

Number Crunch

Starting at the left with the number provided, work across from one box to another, applying the mathematical instructions to your running total.

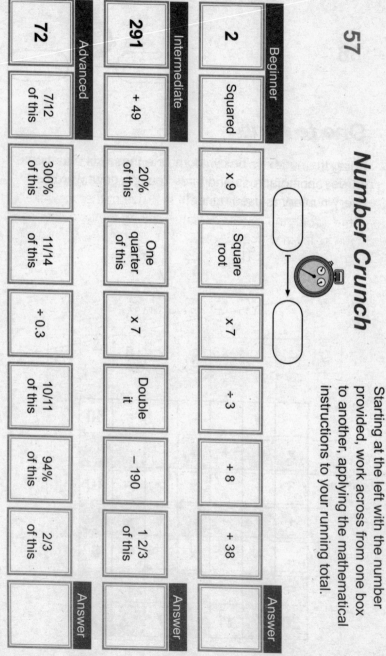

Beginner

| 2 | Squared | x 9 | Square root | x 7 | ÷ 3 | + 8 | + 38 | Answer |

Intermediate

| 291 | + 49 | 20% of this | One quarter of this | x 7 | Double it | − 190 | 1 2/3 of this | Answer |

Advanced

| 72 | 7/12 of this | 300% of this | 11/14 of this | ÷ 0.3 | 10/11 of this | 94% of this | 2/3 of this | Answer |

Summing Up

Arrange one of each of the four given numbers, as well as one each of the symbols – (minus), x (times) and + (plus) in every row and column to arrive at the answer at the end of the row or column, making the calculations in the order in which they appear.

1　3

8　9

9	–	3	+	1	x	8	=	56
						+		=	4
								=	98
						x			
	–							=	90
=		=		=		=			
22		20		78		54			

Isolate

Draw walls to partition the grid into areas (some walls are already drawn in for you). Each area must contain two circles, area sizes must match those shown by the numbers next to the grid and each '+' must be linked to at least two walls.

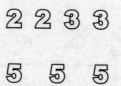

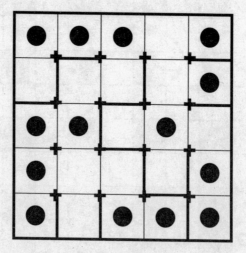

Pyramid Plus

The number in each circle is the sum of the two numbers below it. Just work out the missing numbers in every circle!

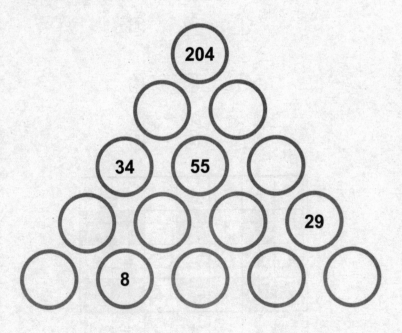

One to Nine

Using the numbers below, complete these six equations (three reading across and three reading downwards). Every number is used once.

	−		+		=	14
−		+		−		
4	+		−		=	9
x		x		+		
	x		+		=	11
=		=		=		
5		60		9		

Number Crunch

Starting at the left with the number provided, work across from one box to another, applying the mathematical instructions to your running total.

Beginner

35	÷ 5	+ 27	× 2	÷ 4	− 8	Square root	× 15	Answer

Intermediate

29	− 14	Squared	÷ 3	1 2/3 of this	4/5 of this	67% of this	+ 88	Answer

Advanced

43	× 7	+ 199	69% of this	9/15 of this	17/23 of this	4/9 of this	× 7	Answer

Summing Up

Arrange one of each of the four given numbers, as well as one each of the symbols – (minus), x (times) and + (plus) in every row and column to arrive at the answer at the end of the row or column, making the calculations in the order in which they appear.

3	x	7	–	5	+	2	=	18
	■		■		■		■	
							=	24
x	■		■		■		■	
			x			7	=	14
	■		■	+	■		■	
							=	15
=	■	=	■	=	■	=	■	
9	■	28	■	34	■	30	■	

Isolate

Draw walls to partition the grid into areas (some walls are already drawn in for you). Each area must contain two circles, area sizes must match those shown by the numbers next to the grid and each '+' must be linked to at least two walls.

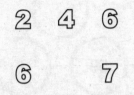

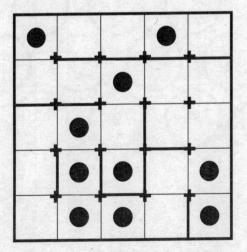

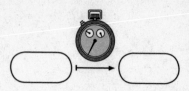

Pyramid Plus

The number in each circle is the sum of the two numbers below it. Just work out the missing numbers in every circle!

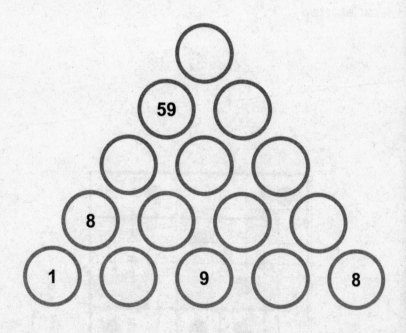

One to Nine

Using the numbers below, complete these six equations (three reading across and three reading downwards). Every number is used once.

	x		–		=	5
+		x		+		
	x	6	+		=	15
x		+		–		
	–		x		=	6
=		=		=		
40		23		14		

Number Crunch

Starting at the left with the number provided, work across from one box to another, applying the mathematical instructions to your running total.

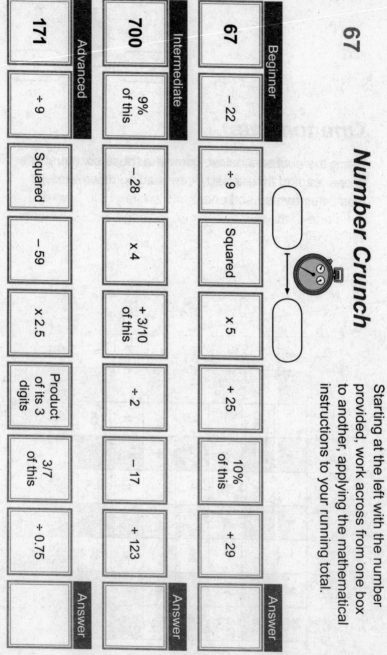

Beginner

| 67 | − 22 | ÷ 9 | Squared | × 5 | + 25 | 10% of this | + 29 | Answer |

Intermediate

| 700 | 9% of this | − 28 | × 4 | + 3/10 of this | ÷ 2 | − 17 | + 123 | Answer |

Advanced

| 171 | ÷ 9 | Squared | − 59 | × 2.5 | Product of its 3 digits | 3/7 of this | ÷ 0.75 | Answer |

Summing Up

Arrange one of each of the four given numbers, as well as one each of the symbols – (minus), x (times) and + (plus) in every row and column to arrive at the answer at the end of the row or column, making the calculations in the order in which they appear.

3   4

7   9

9	–	3	+	4	x	7	=	70
x						–		
							=	96
						x		
							=	64
							=	40
=		=		=		=		
32		86		70		25		

Isolate

Draw walls to partition the grid into areas (some walls are already drawn in for you). Each area must contain two circles, area sizes must match those shown by the numbers next to the grid and each '+' must be linked to at least two walls.

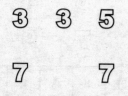

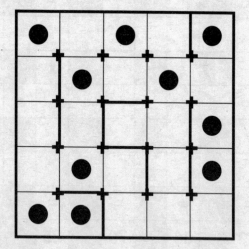

Pyramid Plus

The number in each circle is the sum of the two numbers below it. Just work out the missing numbers in every circle!

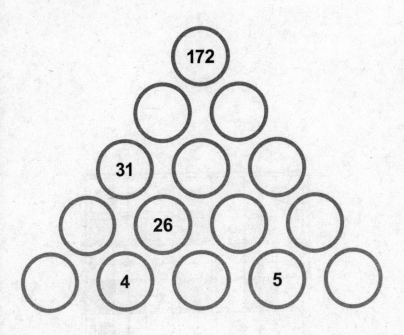

One to Nine

Using the numbers below, complete these six equations (three reading across and three reading downwards). Every number is used once.

	x		–	9	=	1
+		x		–		
	x		+		=	10
–		+		x		
	+		x		=	80
=		=		=		
3		9		48		

Number Crunch

Starting at the left with the number provided, work across from one box to another, applying the mathematical instructions to your running total.

Beginner

| 9 | + 14 | × 2 | − 19 | 2/3 of this | ÷ 9 | + 50% of this | × 7 | Answer |

Intermediate

| 829 | − 555 | Half of this | + 85 | ÷ 37 | This cubed | 3/9 of this | 3/8 of this | Answer |

Advanced

| 256 | ÷ 0.5 | Cube root | × 1.75 | × 2.5 | Squared | 6/49 of this | 68% of this | Answer |

Summing Up

Arrange one of each of the four given numbers, as well as one each of the symbols – (minus), x (times) and + (plus) in every row and column to arrive at the answer at the end of the row or column, making the calculations in the order in which they appear.

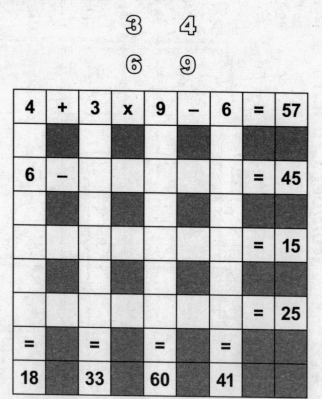

Isolate

Draw walls to partition the grid into areas (some walls are already drawn in for you). Each area must contain two circles, area sizes must match those shown by the numbers next to the grid and each '+' must be linked to at least two walls.

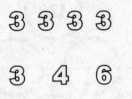

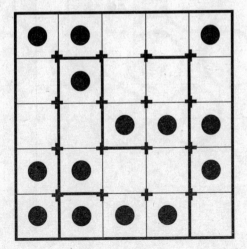

Pyramid Plus

The number in each circle is the sum of the two numbers below it. Just work out the missing numbers in every circle!

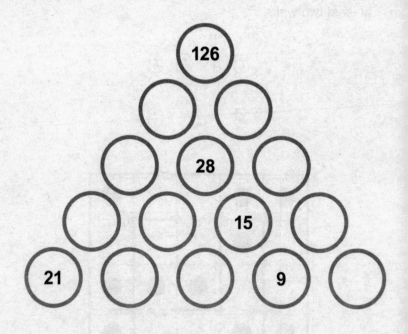

One to Nine

Using the numbers below, complete these six equations (three reading across and three reading downwards). Every number is used once.

1   2   3

4   5   6

7   8   9

	−		+		=	12
−		+		x		
	+	7	x		=	50
+		x		−		
	x		+		=	20
=		=		=		
8		48		12		

Number Crunch

Starting at the left with the number provided, work across from one box to another, applying the mathematical instructions to your running total.

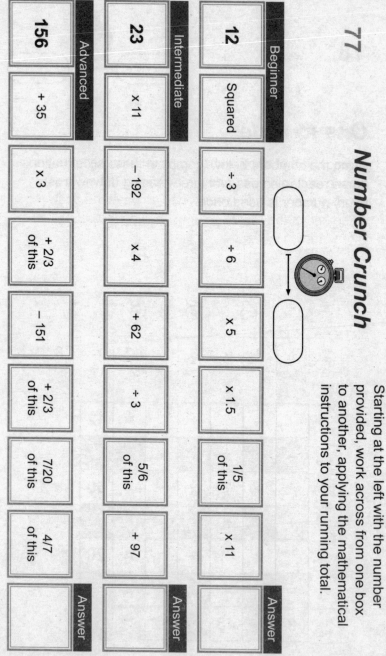

Beginner							
12	Squared	÷ 3	÷ 6	× 5	× 1.5	1/5 of this	× 11	Answer

Intermediate							
23	× 11	− 192	× 4	+ 62	÷ 3	5/6 of this	+ 97	Answer

Advanced							
156	+ 35	× 3	+ 2/3 of this	− 151	+ 2/3 of this	7/20 of this	4/7 of this	Answer

Summing Up

Arrange one of each of the four given numbers, as well as one each of the symbols – (minus), x (times) and + (plus) in every row and column to arrive at the answer at the end of the row or column, making the calculations in the order in which they appear.

2   3

7   8

7	+	3	x	8	–	2	=	78
							=	12
			–		x		=	64
				3			=	25
=		=		=		=		
23		19		27		33		

Isolate

Draw walls to partition the grid into areas (some walls are already drawn in for you). Each area must contain two circles, area sizes must match those shown by the numbers next to the grid and each '+' must be linked to at least two walls.

2   3   3

5   6   6

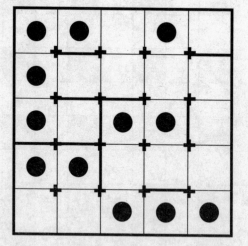

Pyramid Plus

The number in each circle is the sum of the two numbers below it. Just work out the missing numbers in every circle!

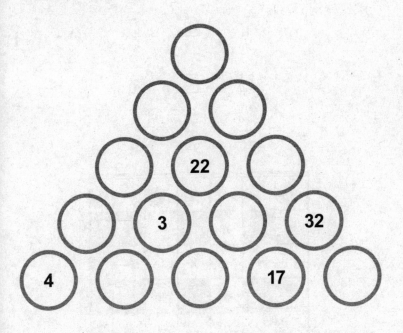

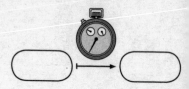

One to Nine

Using the numbers below, complete these six equations (three reading across and three reading downwards). Every number is used once.

1 2 3

4 5 6

7 8 9

	−		x		=	16
+		x		−		
	+		x		=	12
−		+		x		
	x		−	6	=	21
=		=		=		
8		19		42		

Number Crunch

Starting at the left with the number provided, work across from one box to another, applying the mathematical instructions to your running total.

Beginner

| 85 | 1/5 of this | × 2 | + 8 | × 2 | ÷ 7 | + 88 | 24% of this | Answer |

Intermediate

| 456 | 2/3 of this | ÷ 4 | × 1.5 | × 3 | 5/9 of this | Less 10% | 2/19 of this | Answer |

Advanced

| 285 | 15/19 of this | Square root | ÷ 0.75 | × 23 | + 20% of this | + 1/3 of this | × 0.875 | Answer |

83

Summing Up

Arrange one of each of the four given numbers, as well as one each of the symbols – (minus), x (times) and + (plus) in every row and column to arrive at the answer at the end of the row or column, making the calculations in the order in which they appear.

1 4

6 9

4	+	6	–	1	x	9	=	81
				6			=	11
							=	19
9							=	34
=		=		=		=		
27		57		59		36		

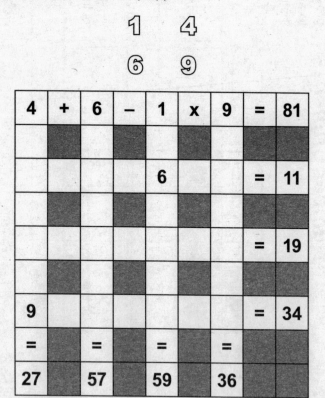

Isolate

Draw walls to partition the grid into areas (some walls are already drawn in for you). Each area must contain two circles, area sizes must match those shown by the numbers next to the grid and each '+' must be linked to at least two walls.

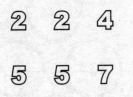

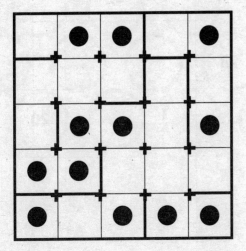

Pyramid Plus

The number in each circle is the sum of the two numbers below it. Just work out the missing numbers in every circle!

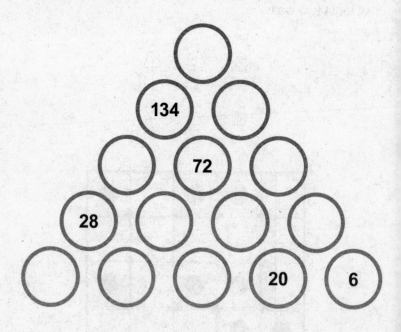

One to Nine

Using the numbers below, complete these six equations (three reading across and three reading downwards). Every number is used once.

	x	7	+		=	11
+		+		x		
	x		−		=	42
−		x		+		
	+		x		=	64
=		=		=		
4		96		20		

87

Number Crunch

Starting at the left with the number provided, work across from one box to another, applying the mathematical instructions to your running total.

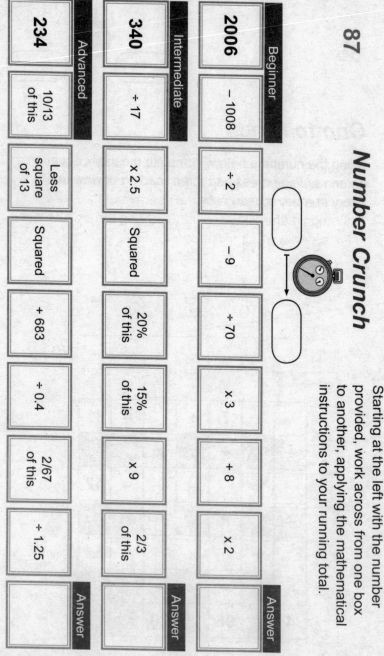

Beginner							
2006	− 1008	÷ 2	− 9	÷ 70	x 3	+ 8	x 2

Answer

Intermediate							
340	÷ 17	x 2.5	Squared	20% of this	15% of this	x 9	2/3 of this

Answer

Advanced							
234	10/13 of this	Less square of 13	Squared	+ 683	÷ 0.4	2/67 of this	÷ 1.25

Answer

92

Summing Up

Arrange one of each of the four given numbers, as well as one each of the symbols – (minus), x (times) and + (plus) in every row and column to arrive at the answer at the end of the row or column, making the calculations in the order in which they appear.

3 5

7 8

3	+	8	–	7	x	5	=	20
							=	40
		x						
				5			=	42
							=	16
=		=		=		=		
14		8		54		57		

93

Isolate

Draw walls to partition the grid into areas (some walls are already drawn in for you). Each area must contain two circles, area sizes must match those shown by the numbers next to the grid and each '+' must be linked to at least two walls.

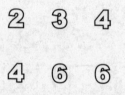

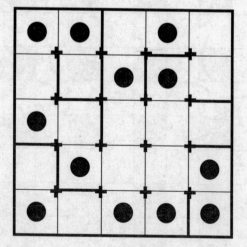

Pyramid Plus

The number in each circle is the sum of the two numbers below it. Just work out the missing numbers in every circle!

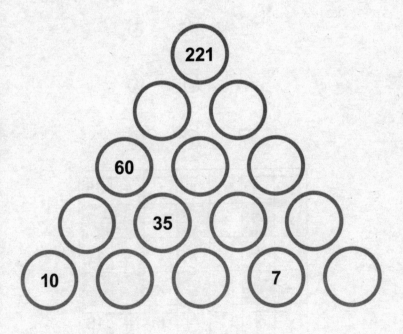

One to Nine

Using the numbers below, complete these six equations (three reading across and three reading downwards). Every number is used once.

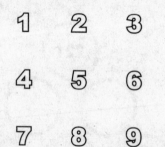

	−		x		=	35
x		+		−		
	+		x		=	11
−		x		x		
	x		−	6	=	18
=		=		=		
33		72		24		

Number Crunch

Starting at the left with the number provided, work across from one box to another, applying the mathematical instructions to your running total.

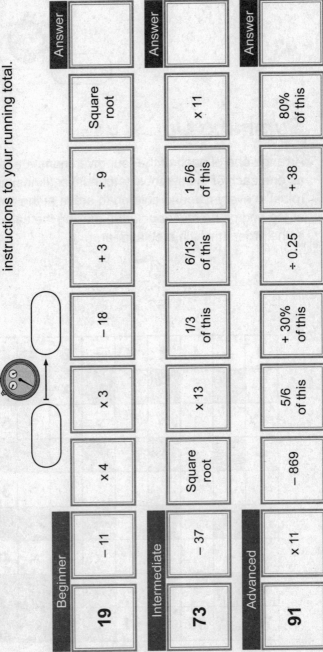

Beginner

| 19 | × 4 | × 3 | − 18 | + 3 | ÷ 9 | Square root | Answer |

Intermediate

| 73 | − 37 | Square root | × 13 | 1/3 of this | 6/13 of this | 1 5/6 of this | × 11 | Answer |

Advanced

| 91 | × 11 | − 869 | 5/6 of this | + 30% of this | ÷ 0.25 | + 38 | 80% of this | Answer |

Summing Up

Arrange one of each of the four given numbers, as well as one each of the symbols – (minus), x (times) and + (plus) in every row and column to arrive at the answer at the end of the row or column, making the calculations in the order in which they appear.

9	–	4	x	7	+	6	=	41
						x		
							=	53
–								
							=	31
	–				x		=	40
=		=		=		=		
77		35		81		37		

Isolate

Draw walls to partition the grid into areas (some walls are already drawn in for you). Each area must contain two circles, area sizes must match those shown by the numbers next to the grid and each '+' must be linked to at least two walls.

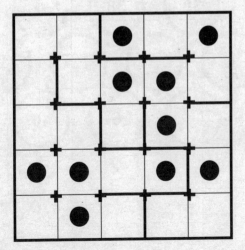

Pyramid Plus

The number in each circle is the sum of the two numbers below it. Just work out the missing numbers in every circle!

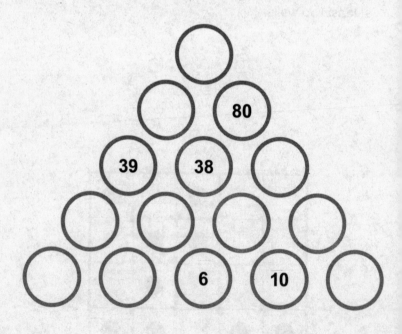

One to Nine

Using the numbers below, complete these six equations
(three reading across and three reading downwards).
Every number is used once.

1	+		x		=	45
x		+		−		
	x		−		=	40
+		x		+		
	−		+		=	10
=		=		=		
12		30		15		

Number Crunch

Starting at the left with the number provided, work across from one box to another, applying the mathematical instructions to your running total.

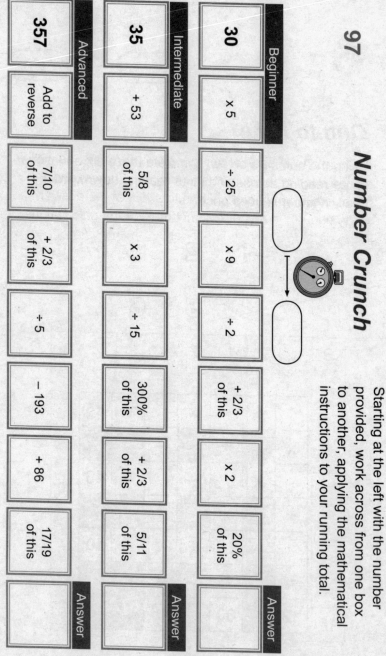

Beginner

| 30 | × 5 | ÷ 25 | × 9 | ÷ 2 | + 2/3 of this | × 2 | 20% of this | Answer |

Intermediate

| 35 | + 53 | 5/8 of this | × 3 | ÷ 15 | 300% of this | + 2/3 of this | 5/11 of this | Answer |

Advanced

| 357 | Add to reverse | 7/10 of this | + 2/3 of this | ÷ 5 | − 193 | + 86 | 17/19 of this | Answer |

Summing Up

Arrange one of each of the four given numbers, as well as one each of the symbols – (minus), x (times) and + (plus) in every row and column to arrive at the answer at the end of the row or column, making the calculations in the order in which they appear.

2 5
6 8

6	x	2	+	5	–	8	=	9
				–				
							=	12
			x				=	86
		–						
							=	15
=		=		=		=		
18		8		30		20		

103

Isolate

Draw walls to partition the grid into areas (some walls are already drawn in for you). Each area must contain two circles, area sizes must match those shown by the numbers next to the grid and each '+' must be linked to at least two walls.

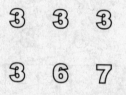

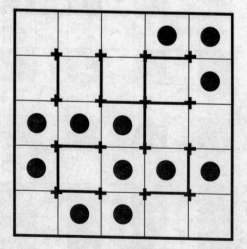

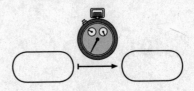

Pyramid Plus

The number in each circle is the sum of the two numbers below it. Just work out the missing numbers in every circle!

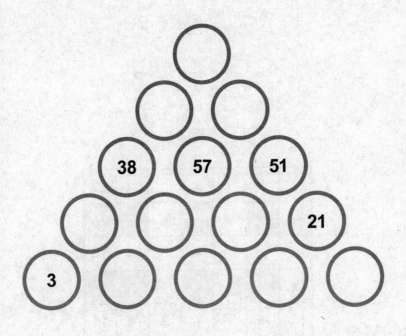

One to Nine

Using the numbers below, complete these six equations (three reading across and three reading downwards). Every number is used once.

1 2 3

4 5 6

7 8 9

	+		x		=	22
−		+		x		
	x		+		=	14
x		−		+		
	+		−	3	=	11
=		=		=		
15		4		19		

Number Crunch

Starting at the left with the number provided, work across from one box to another, applying the mathematical instructions to your running total.

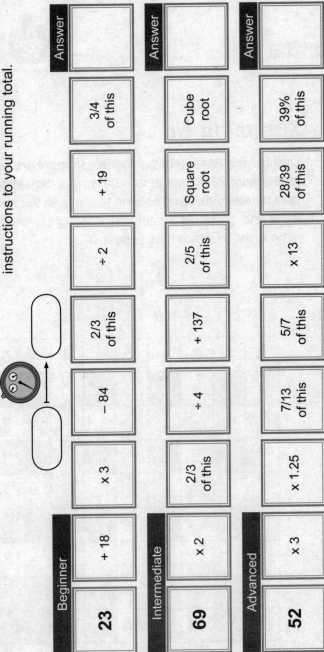

Beginner							Answer
23	+ 18	× 3	− 84	2/3 of this	÷ 2	+ 19	3/4 of this	

Intermediate							Answer
69	× 2	2/3 of this	÷ 4	+ 137	2/5 of this	Square root	Cube root	

Advanced							Answer
52	× 3	× 1.25	7/13 of this	5/7 of this	× 13	28/39 of this	39% of this	

Summing Up

Arrange one of each of the four given numbers, as well as one each of the symbols – (minus), x (times) and + (plus) in every row and column to arrive at the answer at the end of the row or column, making the calculations in the order in which they appear.

9	–	3	+	7	x	4	=	52
		x						
							=	22
							=	24
						7	=	30
=		=		=		=		
61		14		44		16		

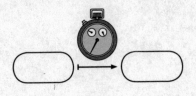

Isolate

Draw walls to partition the grid into areas (some walls are already drawn in for you). Each area must contain two circles, area sizes must match those shown by the numbers next to the grid and each '+' must be linked to at least two walls.

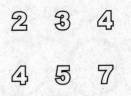

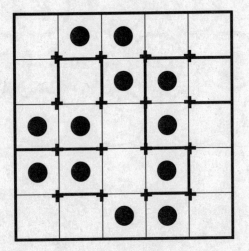

Pyramid Plus

The number in each circle is the sum of the two numbers below it. Just work out the missing numbers in every circle!

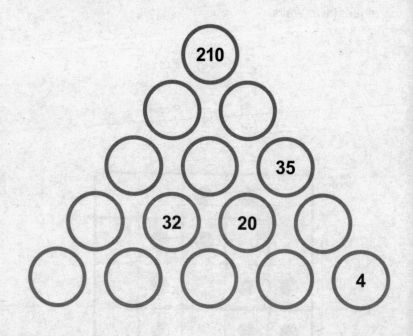

One to Nine

Using the numbers below, complete these six equations
(three reading across and three reading downwards).
Every number is used once.

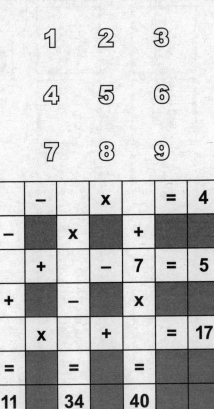

Number Crunch

Starting at the left with the number provided, work across from one box to another, applying the mathematical instructions to your running total.

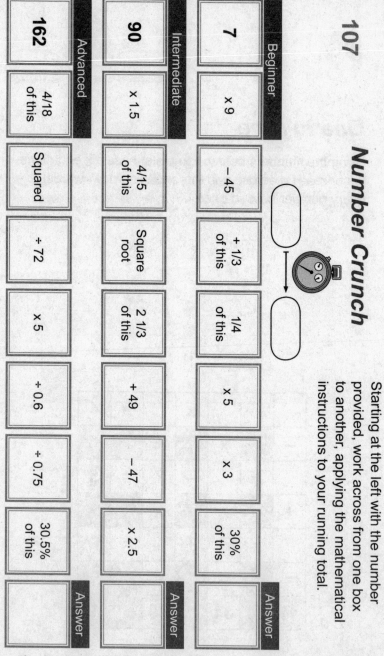

Beginner

| 7 | × 9 | − 45 | + 1/3 of this | 1/4 of this | × 5 | × 3 | 30% of this | Answer |

Intermediate

| 90 | × 1.5 | 4/15 of this | Square root | 2 1/3 of this | + 49 | − 47 | × 2.5 | Answer |

Advanced

| 162 | 4/18 of this | Squared | ÷ 72 | × 5 | ÷ 0.6 | ÷ 0.75 | 30.5% of this | Answer |

Summing Up

Arrange one of each of the four given numbers, as well
as one each of the symbols – (minus), x (times) and +
(plus) in every row and column to arrive at the answer
at the end of the row or column, making the calculations
in the order in which they appear.

2 5

7 8

8	+	2	x	5	–	7	=	43
		x						
							=	41
7							=	18
							=	65
=		=		=		=		
23		17		77		25		

Isolate

Draw walls to partition the grid into areas (some walls are already drawn in for you). Each area must contain two circles, area sizes must match those shown by the numbers next to the grid and each '+' must be linked to at least two walls.

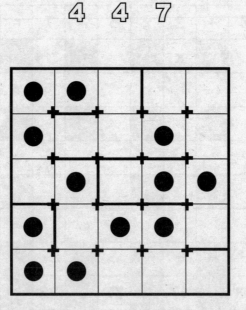

Pyramid Plus

The number in each circle is the sum of the two numbers below it. Just work out the missing numbers in every circle!

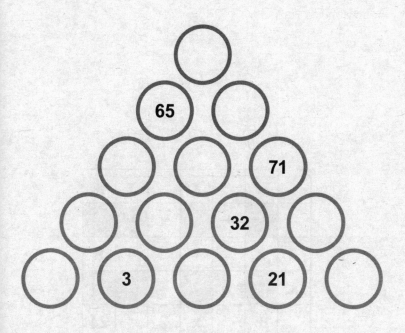

One to Nine

Using the numbers below, complete these six equations (three reading across and three reading downwards). Every number is used once.

Number Crunch

112

Starting at the left with the number provided, work across from one box to another, applying the mathematical instructions to your running total.

Beginner

| 17 | × 2 | + 28 | − 14 | ÷ 3 | × 5 | × 1.25 | 14% of this | Answer |

Intermediate

| 501 | − 180 | 2/3 of this | Double it | 1 3/4 of this | − 627 | + 178 | 22% of this | Answer |

Advanced

| 62 | × 9 | 15/18 of this | 8/15 of this | 5/8 of this | 1 4/5 of this | 1 2/9 of this | − 192 | Answer |

Summing Up

Arrange one of each of the four given numbers, as well as one each of the symbols – (minus), x (times) and + (plus) in every row and column to arrive at the answer at the end of the row or column, making the calculations in the order in which they appear.

7	+	3	x	1	–	8	=	2
				3			=	12
							=	14
x								
							=	52
=		=		=		=		
72		30		25		4		

Isolate

Draw walls to partition the grid into areas (some walls
are already drawn in for you). Each area must contain
two circles, area sizes must match those shown by the
numbers next to the grid and each '+' must be linked to
at least two walls.

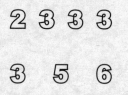

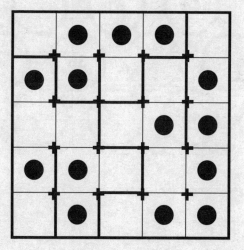

Pyramid Plus

The number in each circle is the sum of the two numbers below it. Just work out the missing numbers in every circle!

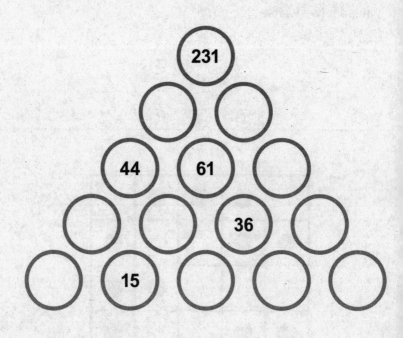

One to Nine

Using the numbers below, complete these six equations
(three reading across and three reading downwards).
Every number is used once.

1   2   3

4   5   6

7   8   9

	−		x	6	=	30
+		x		−		
	+		−		=	8
x		−		x		
	+		x		=	27
=		=		=		
26		20		18		

Number Crunch

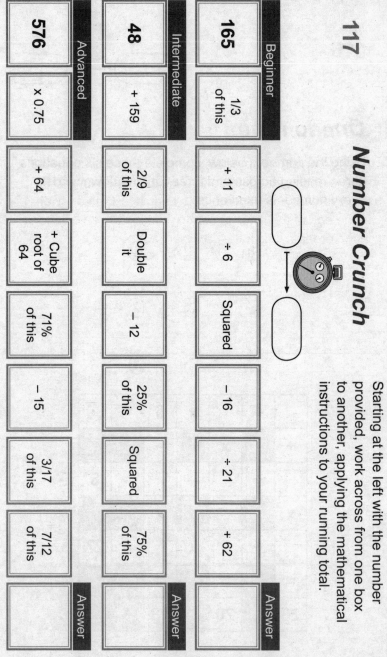

Starting at the left with the number provided, work across from one box to another, applying the mathematical instructions to your running total.

Beginner

| 165 | 1/3 of this | + 11 | ÷ 6 | Squared | − 16 | ÷ 21 | + 62 | Answer |

Intermediate

| 48 | + 159 | 2/9 of this | Double it | − 12 | 25% of this | Squared | 75% of this | Answer |

Advanced

| 576 | × 0.75 | + 64 | + Cube root of 64 | 71% of this | − 15 | 3/17 of this | 7/12 of this | Answer |

122

Summing Up

Arrange one of each of the four given numbers, as well as one each of the symbols – (minus), x (times) and + (plus) in every row and column to arrive at the answer at the end of the row or column, making the calculations in the order in which they appear.

2 5

6 9

2	+	9	x	6	–	5	=	61
	–						=	72
							=	17
+								
							=	37
=		=		=		=		
7		47		73		81		

Isolate

Draw walls to partition the grid into areas (some walls are already drawn in for you). Each area must contain two circles, area sizes must match those shown by the numbers next to the grid and each '+' must be linked to at least two walls.

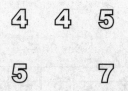

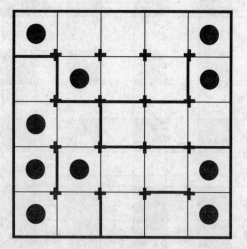

Pyramid Plus

The number in each circle is the sum of the two numbers below it. Just work out the missing numbers in every circle!

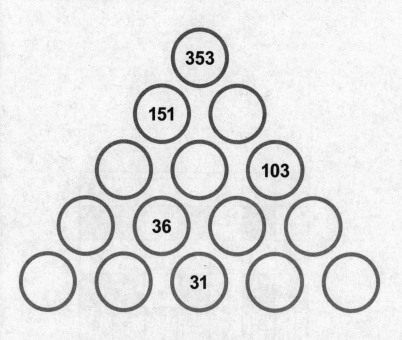

One to Nine

Using the numbers below, complete these six equations (three reading across and three reading downwards). Every number is used once.

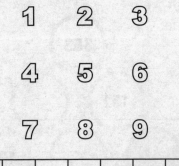

1   2   3

4   5   6

7   8   9

	x		−		=	28
+		−		x		
4	−		x		=	27
x		x		+		
	+		−		=	4
=		=		=		
80		12		25		

Number Crunch

Starting at the left with the number provided, work across from one box to another, applying the mathematical instructions to your running total.

Beginner

| 94 | + 6 | Square root | + 25 | ÷ 7 | | Squared | × 7 | + 13 | Answer |

Intermediate

| 64 | 12.5% of this | × 21 | 2/3 of this | 75% of this | ÷ 7 | × 13 | 5/6 of this | Answer |

Advanced

| 476 | ÷ 28 | Squared | × 3 | − 292 | 19/23 of this | ÷ 0.76 | Divide by 5 cubed | Answer |

Summing Up

Arrange one of each of the four given numbers, as well as one each of the symbols – (minus), x (times) and + (plus) in every row and column to arrive at the answer at the end of the row or column, making the calculations in the order in which they appear.

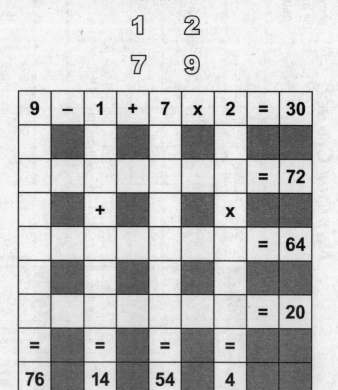

1 2

7 9

9	–	1	+	7	x	2	=	30
							=	72
		+				x		
							=	64
							=	20
=		=		=		=		
76		14		54		4		

Isolate

Draw walls to partition the grid into areas (some walls are already drawn in for you). Each area must contain two circles, area sizes must match those shown by the numbers next to the grid and each '+' must be linked to at least two walls.

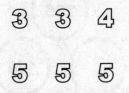

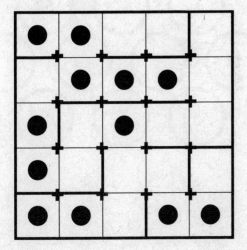

Pyramid Plus

The number in each circle is the sum of the two numbers below it. Just work out the missing numbers in every circle!

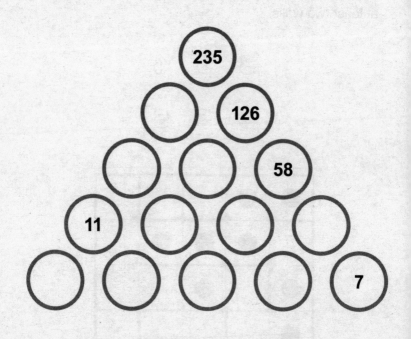

One to Nine

Using the numbers below, complete these six equations
(three reading across and three reading downwards).
Every number is used once.

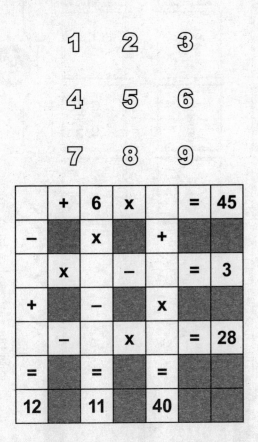

Number Crunch

Starting at the left with the number provided, work across from one box to another, applying the mathematical instructions to your running total.

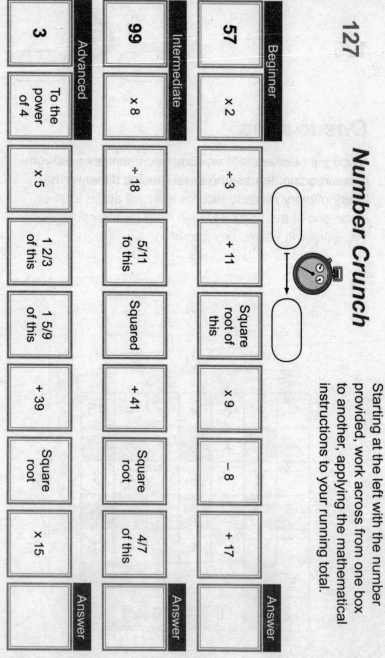

Beginner

| 57 | × 2 | + 3 | + 11 | Square root of this | × 9 | − 8 | + 17 | Answer |

Intermediate

| 99 | × 8 | ÷ 18 | 5/11 fo this | Squared | + 41 | Square root | 4/7 of this | Answer |

Advanced

| 3 | To the power of 4 | × 5 | 1 2/3 of this | 1 5/9 of this | + 39 | Square root | × 15 | Answer |

128

Summing Up

Arrange one of each of the four given numbers, as well as one each of the symbols – (minus), x (times) and + (plus) in every row and column to arrive at the answer at the end of the row or column, making the calculations in the order in which they appear.

4   5

7   9

7	–	4	+	5	x	9	=	72
							=	48
				x				
4							=	94
	–						=	32
=		=		=		=		
39		34		16		44		

133

Isolate

Draw walls to partition the grid into areas (some walls are already drawn in for you). Each area must contain two circles, area sizes must match those shown by the numbers next to the grid and each '+' must be linked to at least two walls.

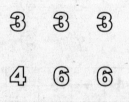

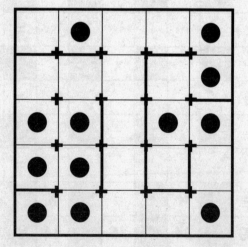

Pyramid Plus

The number in each circle is the sum of the two numbers below it. Just work out the missing numbers in every circle!

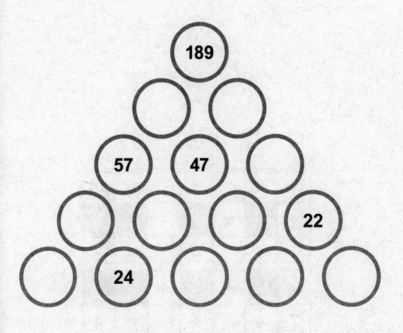

One to Nine

Using the numbers below, complete these six equations (three reading across and three reading downwards). Every number is used once.

1 2 3

4 5 6

7 8 9

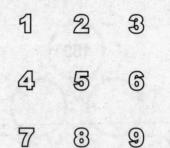

	x		+		=	14
+		x		−		
	+		−		=	8
x		+		+		
7	−		+		=	4
=		=		=		
56		22		3		

Number Crunch

Starting at the left with the number provided, work across from one box to another, applying the mathematical instructions to your running total.

132

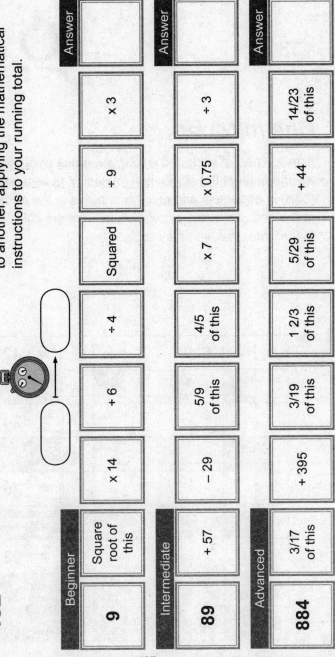

Beginner							Answer
9	Square root of this	× 14	+ 6	÷ 4	Squared	× 3	

Intermediate							Answer
89	+ 57	− 29	5/9 of this	4/5 of this	× 7	× 0.75	÷ 3	

Advanced							Answer
884	3/17 of this	+ 395	3/19 of this	1 2/3 of this	5/29 of this	+ 44	14/23 of this	

Summing Up

Arrange one of each of the four given numbers, as well as one each of the symbols – (minus), x (times) and + (plus) in every row and column to arrive at the answer at the end of the row or column, making the calculations in the order in which they appear.

3   6

7   9

9	–	6	+	3	x	7	=	42
		x						
							=	24
						x		
				7			=	30
							=	93
=		=		=		=		
65		36		78		12		

Isolate

Draw walls to partition the grid into areas (some walls are already drawn in for you). Each area must contain two circles, area sizes must match those shown by the numbers next to the grid and each '+' must be linked to at least two walls.

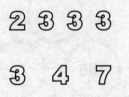

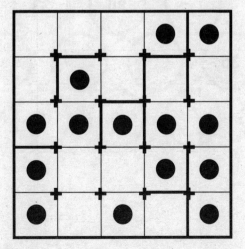

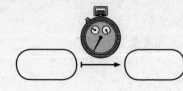

Pyramid Plus

The number in each circle is the sum of the two numbers below it. Just work out the missing numbers in every circle!

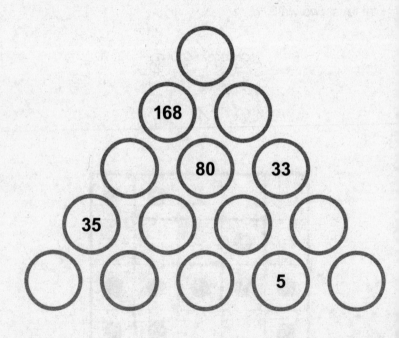

One to Nine

Using the numbers below, complete these six equations
(three reading across and three reading downwards).
Every number is used once.

	x		–		=	10
+		+		x		
	+		–		=	8
x		–		+		
	x		+	8	=	11
=		=		=		
7		13		32		

Number Crunch

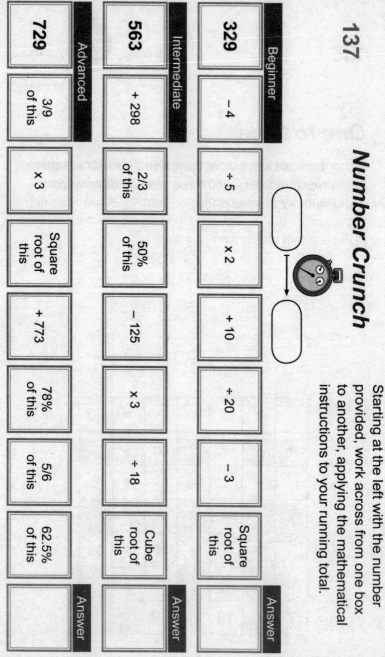

Starting at the left with the number provided, work across from one box to another, applying the mathematical instructions to your running total.

Beginner

| 329 | −4 | ÷ 5 | × 2 | + 10 | + 20 | −3 | Square root of this | Answer |

Intermediate

| 563 | + 298 | 2/3 of this | 50% of this | −125 | × 3 | ÷ 18 | Cube root of this | Answer |

Advanced

| 729 | 3/9 of this | × 3 | Square root of this | + 773 | 78% of this | 5/6 of this | 62.5% of this | Answer |

Summing Up

Arrange one of each of the four given numbers, as well as one each of the symbols – (minus), x (times) and + (plus) in every row and column to arrive at the answer at the end of the row or column, making the calculations in the order in which they appear.

5   7

8   9

5	x	8	–	7	+	9	=	42
				–				
							=	78
					+		=	34
				8			=	21
=		=		=		=		
82		84		26		66		

Isolate

Draw walls to partition the grid into areas (some walls are already drawn in for you). Each area must contain two circles, area sizes must match those shown by the numbers next to the grid and each '+' must be linked to at least two walls.

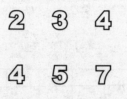

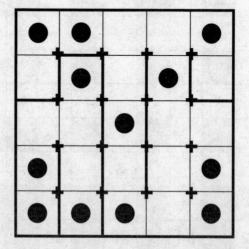

Pyramid Plus

The number in each circle is the sum of the two numbers below it. Just work out the missing numbers in every circle!

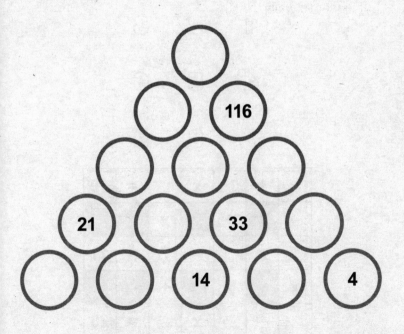

One to Nine

Using the numbers below, complete these six equations (three reading across and three reading downwards). Every number is used once.

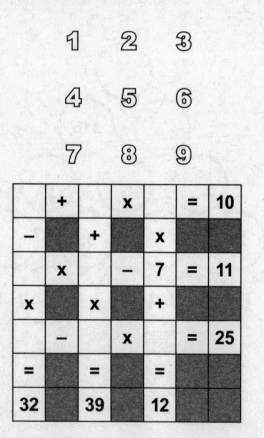

	+		x		=	10
−		+		x		
	x		−	7	=	11
x		x		+		
	−		x		=	25
=		=		=		
32		39		12		

Number Crunch

Starting at the left with the number provided, work across from one box to another, applying the mathematical instructions to your running total.

Beginner

| 87 | One third of this | + 7 | Square root of this | × 9 | − 16 | ÷ 2 | + 15 | Answer |

Intermediate

| 42 | + 19 | × 9 | 2/3 of this | ÷ 3 | + 11 | 4/7 of this | × 4 | Answer |

Advanced

| 997 | × 3 | + 509 | 32% of this | 60% of this | 2/3 of this | 5/16 of this | × 1.75 | Answer |

Summing Up

Arrange one of each of the four given numbers, as well as one each of the symbols – (minus), x (times) and + (plus) in every row and column to arrive at the answer at the end of the row or column, making the calculations in the order in which they appear.

4	+	8	–	1	x	7	=	77
–								
							=	11
		x						
							=	87
			+	7			=	56
=		=		=		=		
29		59		33		53		

Isolate

Draw walls to partition the grid into areas (some walls are already drawn in for you). Each area must contain two circles, area sizes must match those shown by the numbers next to the grid and each '+' must be linked to at least two walls.

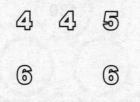

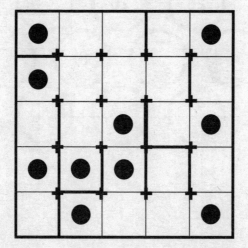

Pyramid Plus

The number in each circle is the sum of the two numbers below it. Just work out the missing numbers in every circle!

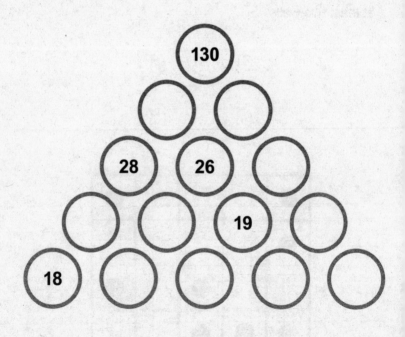

One to Nine

Using the numbers below, complete these six equations
(three reading across and three reading downwards).
Every number is used once.

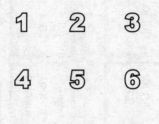

	+	8	x		=	60
x		–		+		
	x		+		=	9
–		x		x		
	–		x		=	42
=		=		=		
1		21		70		

Number Crunch

Starting at the left with the number provided, work across from one box to another, applying the mathematical instructions to your running total.

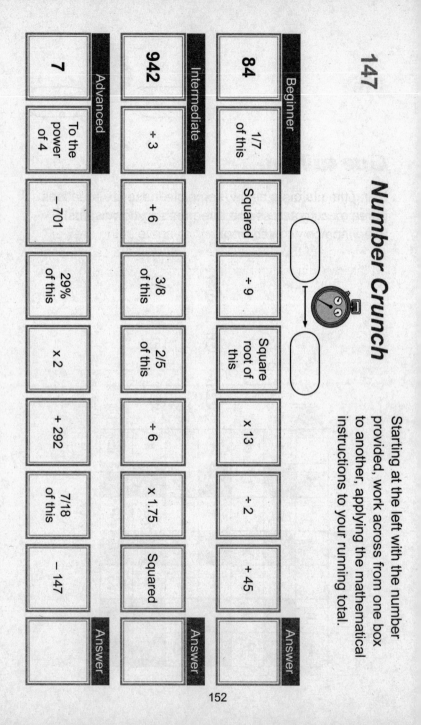

Beginner

| 84 | 1/7 of this | Squared | ÷ 9 | Square root of this | x 13 | ÷ 2 | + 45 | Answer |

Intermediate

| 942 | ÷ 3 | + 6 | 3/8 of this | 2/5 of this | ÷ 6 | x 1.75 | Squared | Answer |

Advanced

| 7 | To the power of 4 | − 701 | 29% of this | x 2 | + 292 | 7/18 of this | − 147 | Answer |

Summing Up

Arrange one of each of the four given numbers, as well as one each of the symbols – (minus), x (times) and + (plus) in every row and column to arrive at the answer at the end of the row or column, making the calculations in the order in which they appear.

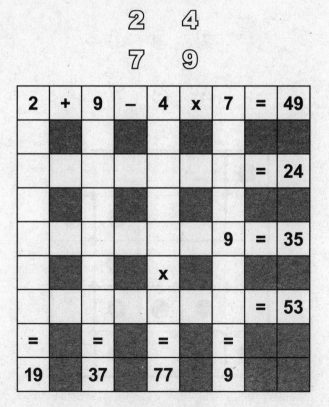

Isolate

Draw walls to partition the grid into areas (some walls are already drawn in for you). Each area must contain two circles, area sizes must match those shown by the numbers next to the grid and each '+' must be linked to at least two walls.

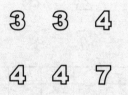

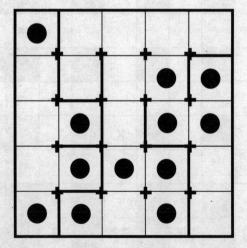

Pyramid Plus

The number in each circle is the sum of the two numbers below it. Just work out the missing numbers in every circle!

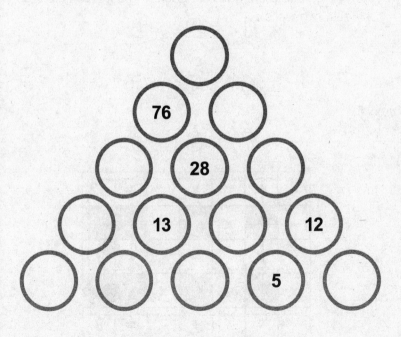

One to Nine

Using the numbers below, complete these six equations (three reading across and three reading downwards). Every number is used once.

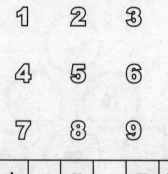

1 2 3

4 5 6

7 8 9

4	+		x		=	12
−		x		+		
	x		−		=	7
x		−		x		
	−		+		=	8
=		=		=		
18		33		24		

Number Crunch

Starting at the left with the number provided, work across from one box to another, applying the mathematical instructions to your running total.

Beginner

76	− 4	÷ 8	Squared	+ 39	One third of this	One quarter of this	Answer

Intermediate

16	Squared	+ 429	4/5 of this	50% of this	× 3	+ 36	− 377	Answer

Advanced

15	× 75	2/3 of this	÷ 25	× 2.6	+ 1/3 of this	37.5% of this	× 1 2/3	Answer

Summing Up

Arrange one of each of the four given numbers, as well as one each of the symbols – (minus), x (times) and + (plus) in every row and column to arrive at the answer at the end of the row or column, making the calculations in the order in which they appear.

5	+	9	x	6	–	8	=	76
				x		+		
							=	17
							=	36
						5	=	25
=		=		=		=		
16		38		44		55		

Isolate

Draw walls to partition the grid into areas (some walls are already drawn in for you). Each area must contain two circles, area sizes must match those shown by the numbers next to the grid and each '+' must be linked to at least two walls.

2 3 4

4 5 7

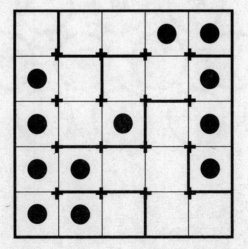

Pyramid Plus

The number in each circle is the sum of the two numbers below it. Just work out the missing numbers in every circle!

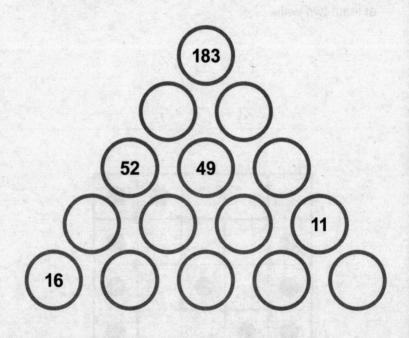

One to Nine

Using the numbers below, complete these six equations
(three reading across and three reading downwards).
Every number is used once.

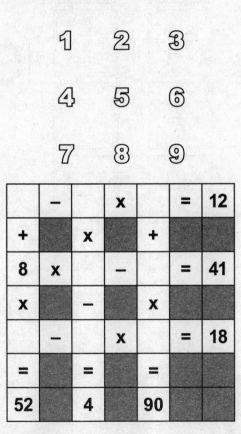

Number Crunch

Starting at the left with the number provided, work across from one box to another, applying the mathematical instructions to your running total.

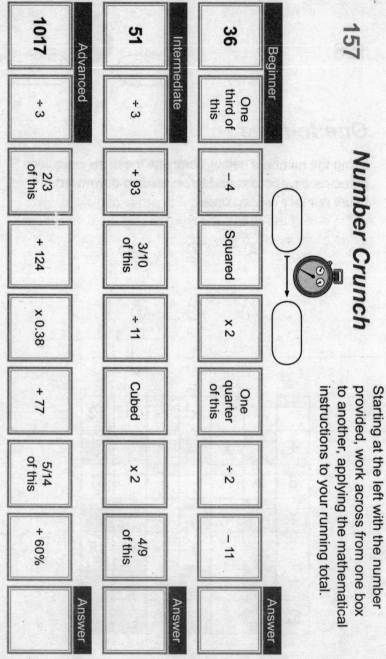

Beginner

| 36 | One third of this | – 4 | Squared | × 2 | One quarter of this | ÷ 2 | – 11 | Answer |

Intermediate

| 51 | ÷ 3 | + 93 | 3/10 of this | ÷ 11 | Cubed | × 2 | 4/9 of this | Answer |

Advanced

| 1017 | ÷ 3 | 2/3 of this | + 124 | × 0.38 | + 77 | 5/14 of this | + 60% | Answer |

Summing Up

Arrange one of each of the four given numbers, as well as one each of the symbols – (minus), x (times) and + (plus) in every row and column to arrive at the answer at the end of the row or column, making the calculations in the order in which they appear.

1   3

6   7

7	–	1	+	3	x	6	=	54
	■		■		■		■	■
							=	62
x	■		■		■		■	■
							=	10
	■				■		■	■
		3	+				=	28
=	■	=	■	=	■	=	■	■
4		46		16		56		

Isolate

Draw walls to partition the grid into areas (some walls
are already drawn in for you). Each area must contain
two circles, area sizes must match those shown by the
numbers next to the grid and each '+' must be linked to
at least two walls.

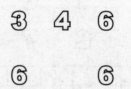

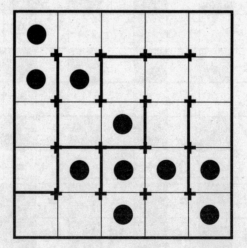

Pyramid Plus

The number in each circle is the sum of the two numbers below it. Just work out the missing numbers in every circle!

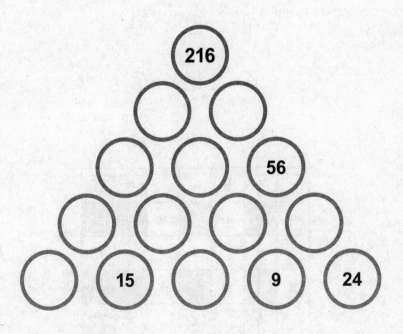

One to Nine

Using the numbers below, complete these six equations (three reading across and three reading downwards). Every number is used once.

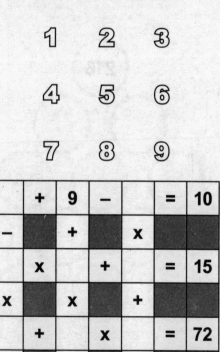

	+	9	–		=	10
–		+		x		
	x		+		=	15
x		x		+		
	+		x		=	72
=		=		=		
9		96		12		

162

Number Crunch

Starting at the left with the number provided, work across from one box to another, applying the mathematical instructions to your running total.

Beginner							Answer
13	Squared	+ 31	One quarter of this	x 5	+ 25	– 125	One third of this

Intermediate							Answer
21	2/7 of this	+ 15	Squared	2/9 of this	+ 4	÷ 17	Cubed

Advanced							Answer
720	87.5% of this	7/18 of this	x 2	9/14 of this	180% of this	÷ 3	+ 5/9 of this

167

Summing Up

Arrange one of each of the four given numbers, as well as one each of the symbols – (minus), x (times) and + (plus) in every row and column to arrive at the answer at the end of the row or column, making the calculations in the order in which they appear.

7	+	9	–	2	x	3	=	42
	x						=	20
							=	44
				9			=	38
=		=		=		=		
48		10		26		32		

Isolate

Draw walls to partition the grid into areas (some walls are already drawn in for you). Each area must contain two circles, area sizes must match those shown by the numbers next to the grid and each '+' must be linked to at least two walls.

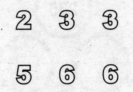

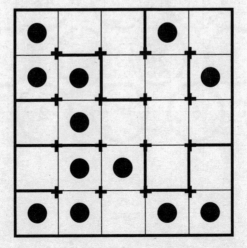

Pyramid Plus

The number in each circle is the sum of the two numbers below it. Just work out the missing numbers in every circle!

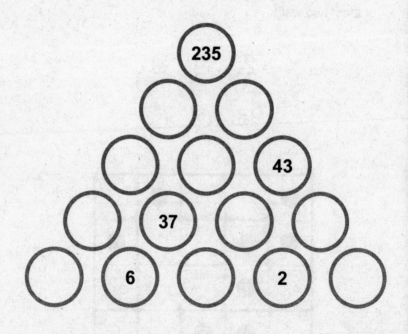

One to Nine

Using the numbers below, complete these six equations (three reading across and three reading downwards). Every number is used once.

1 2 3

4 5 6

7 8 9

	+		x		=	30
−		x		+		
	x		−	5	=	3
x		+		x		
	−		x		=	35
=		=		=		
18		20		77		

Number Crunch

Starting at the left with the number provided, work across from one box to another, applying the mathematical instructions to your running total.

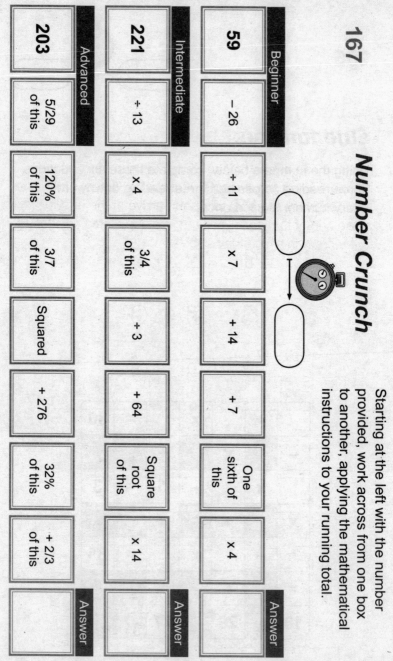

Beginner

| 59 | − 26 | + 11 | × 7 | + 14 | + 7 | One sixth of this | × 4 | Answer |

Intermediate

| 221 | ÷ 13 | × 4 | 3/4 of this | ÷ 3 | + 64 | Square root of this | × 14 | Answer |

Advanced

| 203 | 5/29 of this | 120% of this | 3/7 of this | Squared | + 276 | 32% of this | + 2/3 of this | Answer |

Summing Up

Arrange one of each of the four given numbers, as well as one each of the symbols – (minus), x (times) and + (plus) in every row and column to arrive at the answer at the end of the row or column, making the calculations in the order in which they appear.

3 5
7 9

3	+	9	–	7	x	5	=	25
	–						=	21
						+		
							=	37
							=	29
=		=		=		=		
17		19		77		81		

Isolate

Draw walls to partition the grid into areas (some walls are already drawn in for you). Each area must contain two circles, area sizes must match those shown by the numbers next to the grid and each '+' must be linked to at least two walls.

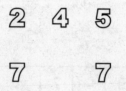

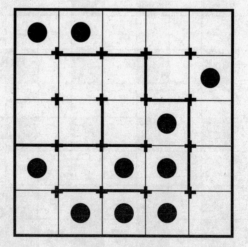

Pyramid Plus

The number in each circle is the sum of the two numbers below it. Just work out the missing numbers in every circle!

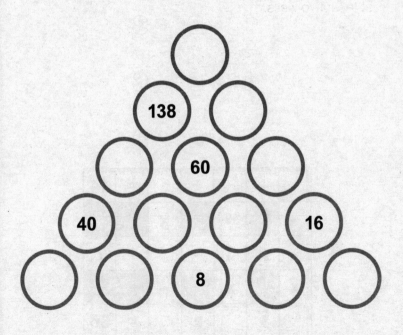

One to Nine

Using the numbers below, complete these six equations
(three reading across and three reading downwards).
Every number is used once.

1 2 3

4 5 6

7 8 9

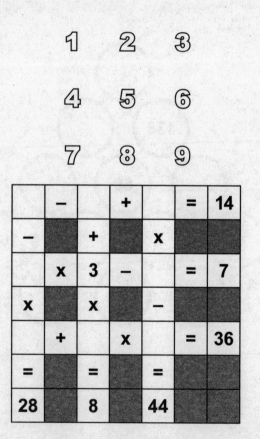

	−		+		=	14
−		+		x		
	x	3	−		=	7
x		x		−		
	+		x		=	36
=		=		=		
28		8		44		

Number Crunch

Starting at the left with the number provided, work across from one box to another, applying the mathematical instructions to your running total.

Beginner

75	× 7	÷ 25	÷ 7	× 16	One sixth of this	÷ 4	× 98	Answer

Intermediate

7	Cubed	+ 7	+ 10%	× 0.4	× 2	× 0.75	+ 169	Answer

Advanced

67	+ 28	8/19 of this	90% of this	+ Square root of this	900% of this	7/18 of this	1 2/3 of this	Answer

Summing Up

Arrange one of each of the four given numbers, as well as one each of the symbols – (minus), x (times) and + (plus) in every row and column to arrive at the answer at the end of the row or column, making the calculations in the order in which they appear.

4	x	6	–	8	+	5	=	21
+								
			x			6	=	18
							=	36
		+						
							=	14
=		=		=		=		
30		12		26		34		

Isolate

Draw walls to partition the grid into areas (some walls are already drawn in for you). Each area must contain two circles, area sizes must match those shown by the numbers next to the grid and each '+' must be linked to at least two walls.

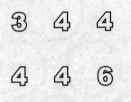

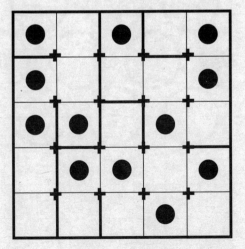

Pyramid Plus

The number in each circle is the sum of the two numbers below it. Just work out the missing numbers in every circle!

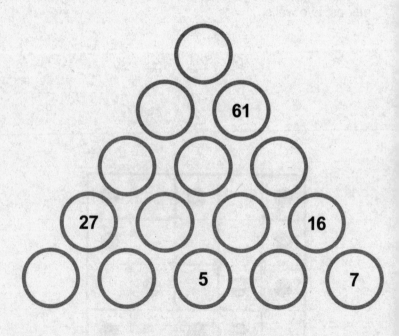

One to Nine

Using the numbers below, complete these six equations
(three reading across and three reading downwards).
Every number is used once.

	+		x		=	44
−		+		x		
	x		−		=	15
x		−		+		
	−	1	x		=	48
=		=		=		
21		14		20		

181

Number Crunch

Starting at the left with the number provided, work across from one box to another, applying the mathematical instructions to your running total.

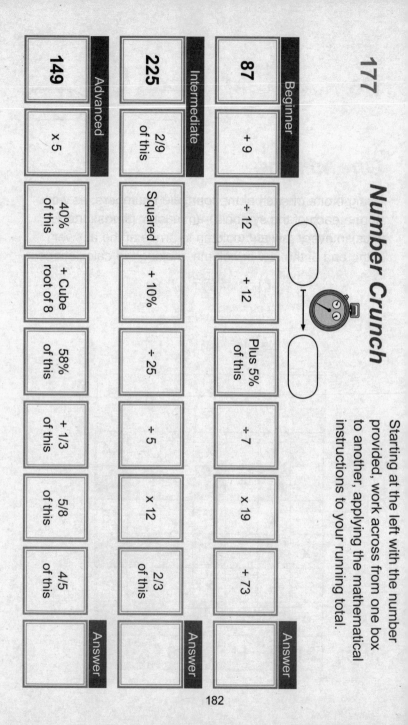

Beginner

| 87 | + 9 | ÷ 12 | + 12 | Plus 5% of this | ÷ 7 | x 19 | + 73 | Answer |

Intermediate

| 225 | 2/9 of this | Squared | + 10% | ÷ 25 | ÷ 5 | x 12 | 2/3 of this | Answer |

Advanced

| 149 | x 5 | 40% of this | + Cube root of 8 | 58% of this | + 1/3 of this | 5/8 of this | 4/5 of this | Answer |

178

Summing Up

Arrange one of each of the four given numbers, as well as one each of the symbols – (minus), x (times) and + (plus) in every row and column to arrive at the answer at the end of the row or column, making the calculations in the order in which they appear.

1 5

6 8

5	+	8	–	1	x	6	=	72
1			+				=	3
		6					=	11
							=	65
=		=		=		=		
38		35		27		52		

Isolate

Draw walls to partition the grid into areas (some walls are already drawn in for you). Each area must contain two circles, area sizes must match those shown by the numbers next to the grid and each '+' must be linked to at least two walls.

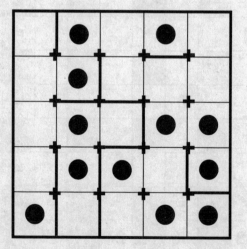

Pyramid Plus

The number in each circle is the sum of the two numbers below it. Just work out the missing numbers in every circle!

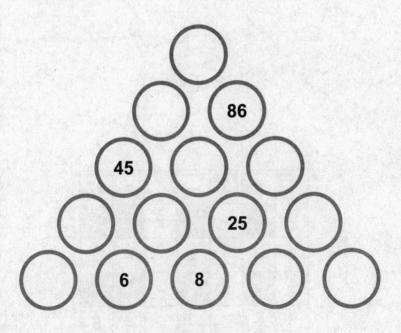

One to Nine

Using the numbers below, complete these six equations (three reading across and three reading downwards). Every number is used once.

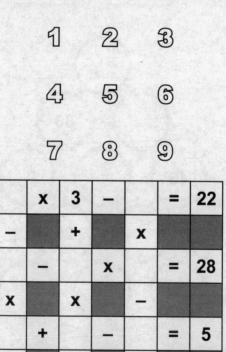

182

Number Crunch

Starting at the left with the number provided, work across from one box to another, applying the mathematical instructions to your running total.

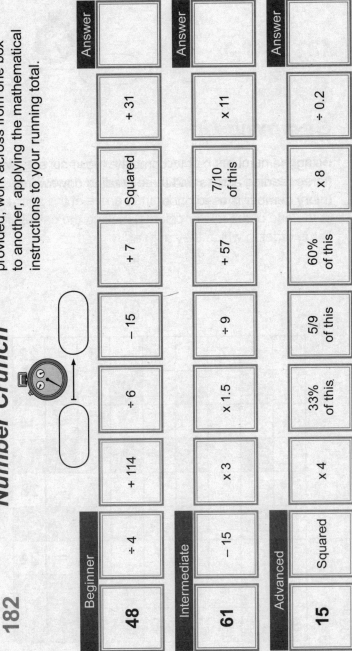

Beginner							Answer
48	÷ 4	+ 114	÷ 6	− 15	+ 7	Squared	+ 31	

Intermediate							Answer
61	− 15	x 3	x 1.5	÷ 9	+ 57	7/10 of this	x 11	

Advanced							Answer
15	Squared	x 4	33% of this	5/9 of this	60% of this	x 8	÷ 0.2	

187

Summing Up

Arrange one of each of the four given numbers, as well as one each of the symbols – (minus), x (times) and + (plus) in every row and column to arrive at the answer at the end of the row or column, making the calculations in the order in which they appear.

3   7

8   9

3	x	7	+	9	–	8	=	22
		–						
							=	44
				+				
						7	=	28
							=	24
=		=		=		=		
92		41		40		30		

Isolate

Draw walls to partition the grid into areas (some walls are already drawn in for you). Each area must contain two circles, area sizes must match those shown by the numbers next to the grid and each '+' must be linked to at least two walls.

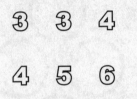

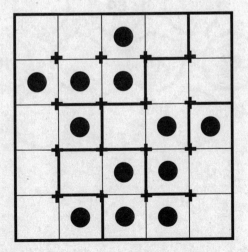

Pyramid Plus

The number in each circle is the sum of the two numbers below it. Just work out the missing numbers in every circle!

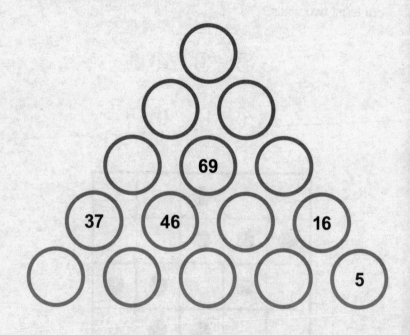

One to Nine

Using the numbers below, complete these six equations (three reading across and three reading downwards). Every number is used once.

	x		–		=	35
+		–		x		
7	–		x		=	30
x		+		–		
	+		–		=	10
=		=		=		
55		15		3		

Number Crunch

Starting at the left with the number provided, work across from one box to another, applying the mathematical instructions to your running total.

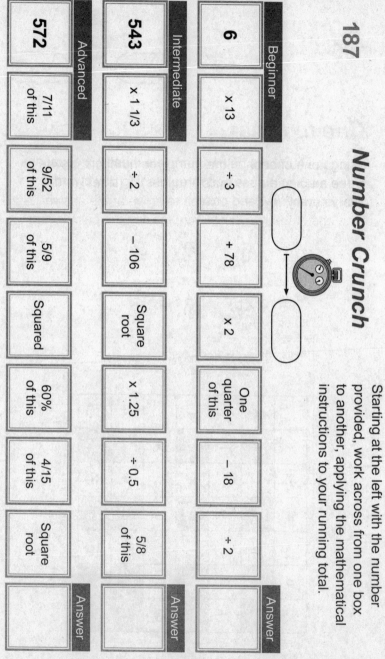

Beginner

| 6 | × 13 | ÷ 3 | + 78 | × 2 | One quarter of this | – 18 | ÷ 2 | Answer |

Intermediate

| 543 | × 1 1/3 | ÷ 2 | – 106 | Square root | × 1.25 | ÷ 0.5 | 5/8 of this | Answer |

Advanced

| 572 | 7/11 of this | 9/52 of this | 5/9 of this | Squared | 60% of this | 4/15 of this | Square root | Answer |

188

Summing Up

Arrange one of each of the four given numbers, as well as one each of the symbols – (minus), x (times) and + (plus) in every row and column to arrive at the answer at the end of the row or column, making the calculations in the order in which they appear.

2 4

6 8

4	+	8	–	2	x	6	=	60
x								
							=	8
							=	48
	+			8			=	78
=		=		=		=		
10		16		28		46		

Isolate

Draw walls to partition the grid into areas (some walls are already drawn in for you). Each area must contain two circles, area sizes must match those shown by the numbers next to the grid and each '+' must be linked to at least two walls.

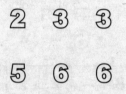

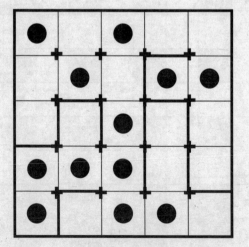

Pyramid Plus

The number in each circle is the sum of the two numbers below it. Just work out the missing numbers in every circle!

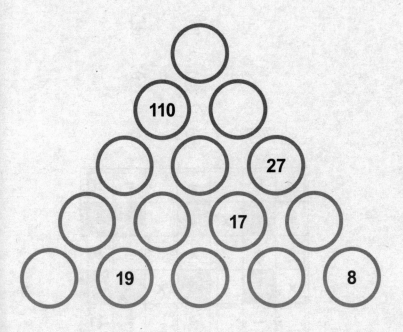

One to Nine

Using the numbers below, complete these six equations (three reading across and three reading downwards). Every number is used once.

1   2   3

4   5   6

7   8   9

	x		+		=	10
+		x		−		
	+		x	5	=	70
x		−		x		
	−		+		=	11
=		=		=		
36		6		18		

192

Number Crunch

Starting at the left with the number provided, work across from one box to another, applying the mathematical instructions to your running total.

Beginner								Answer
187	− 16	÷ 9	− 4	Squared	÷ 25	+ 5	+ 73	

Intermediate								Answer
269	+ 47	÷ 4	× 3	− 88	+ 27	5/8 of this	+ 10%	

Advanced								Answer
631	× 5	+ 60%	÷ 2	× 3.75	6/15 of this	+ 214	73% of this	

197

Summing Up

Arrange one of each of the four given numbers, as well as one each of the symbols – (minus), x (times) and + (plus) in every row and column to arrive at the answer at the end of the row or column, making the calculations in the order in which they appear.

3   4

7   8

4	+	7	–	8	x	3	=	9
			x			7	=	27
	x						=	57
			x				=	41
=		=		=		=		
28		36		49		32		

194

Isolate

Draw walls to partition the grid into areas (some walls are already drawn in for you). Each area must contain two circles, area sizes must match those shown by the numbers next to the grid and each '+' must be linked to at least two walls.

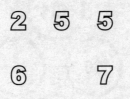

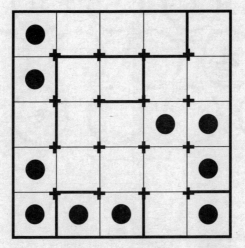

Pyramid Plus

The number in each circle is the sum of the two numbers below it. Just work out the missing numbers in every circle!

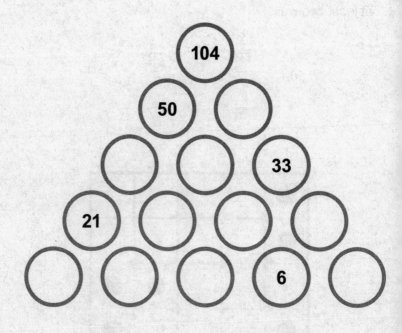

196

One to Nine

Using the numbers below, complete these six equations
(three reading across and three reading downwards).
Every number is used once.

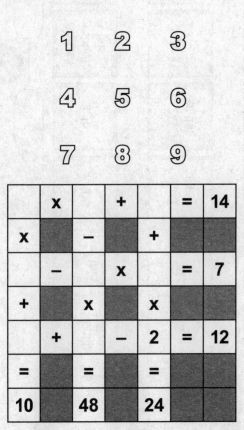

Number Crunch

Starting at the left with the number provided, work across from one box to another, applying the mathematical instructions to your running total.

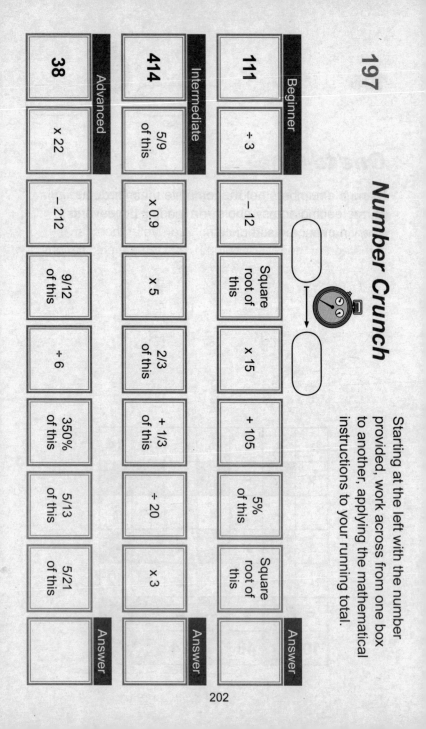

Beginner

| 111 | ÷ 3 | − 12 | Square root of this | × 15 | + 105 | 5% of this | Square root of this | Answer |

Intermediate

| 414 | 5/9 of this | × 0.9 | × 5 | 2/3 of this | + 1/3 of this | ÷ 20 | × 3 | Answer |

Advanced

| 38 | × 22 | − 212 | 9/12 of this | ÷ 6 | 350% of this | 5/13 of this | 5/21 of this | Answer |

Summing Up

Arrange one of each of the four given numbers, as well as one each of the symbols – (minus), x (times) and + (plus) in every row and column to arrive at the answer at the end of the row or column, making the calculations in the order in which they appear.

3 5

6 9

5	x	3	–	9	+	6	=	12
						x		
							=	14
		–						
		5					=	27
							=	40
=		=		=		=		
24		36		42		56		

Isolate

Draw walls to partition the grid into areas (some walls
are already drawn in for you). Each area must contain
two circles, area sizes must match those shown by the
numbers next to the grid and each '+' must be linked to
at least two walls.

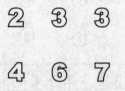

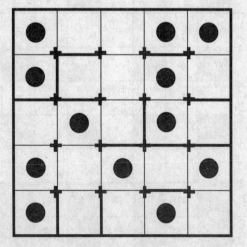

Pyramid Plus

The number in each circle is the sum of the two numbers below it. Just work out the missing numbers in every circle!

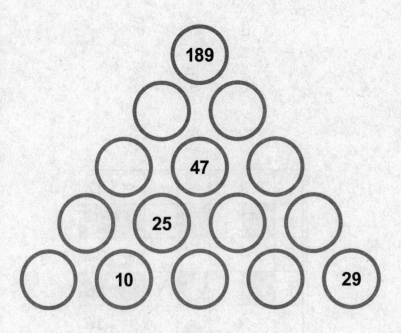

201

One to Nine

Using the numbers below, complete these six equations
(three reading across and three reading downwards).
Every number is used once.

1 2 3

4 5 6

7 8 9

	+		−		=	12
x		−		+		
3	x		+		=	30
+		x		x		
	−		x		=	16
=		=		=		
21		2		40		

206

Number Crunch

Starting at the left with the number provided, work across from one box to another, applying the mathematical instructions to your running total.

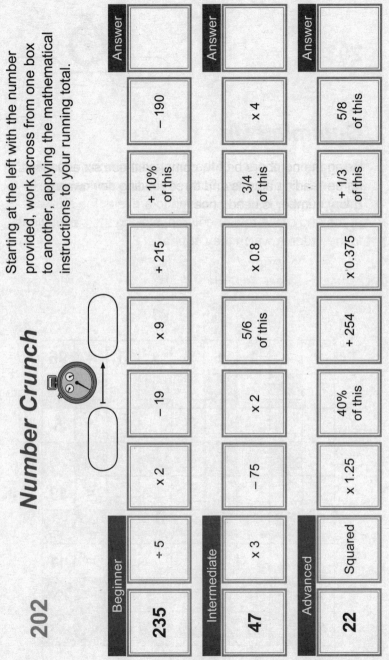

Beginner								Answer
235	÷ 5	× 2	− 19	× 9	+ 215	+ 10% of this	− 190	

Intermediate								Answer
47	× 3	− 75	× 2	5/6 of this	× 0.8	3/4 of this	× 4	

Advanced								Answer
22	Squared	× 1.25	40% of this	+ 254	× 0.375	+ 1/3 of this	5/8 of this	

Summing Up

Arrange one of each of the four given numbers, as well as one each of the symbols – (minus), x (times) and + (plus) in every row and column to arrive at the answer at the end of the row or column, making the calculations in the order in which they appear.

9	–	1	+	8	x	6	=	96
				1			=	5
							=	19
	x						=	11
=		=		=		=		
47		27		69		61		

Isolate

Draw walls to partition the grid into areas (some walls are already drawn in for you). Each area must contain two circles, area sizes must match those shown by the numbers next to the grid and each '+' must be linked to at least two walls.

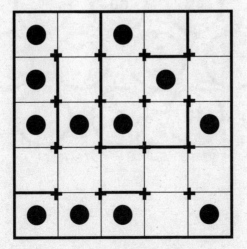

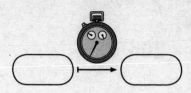

Pyramid Plus

The number in each circle is the sum of the two numbers below it. Just work out the missing numbers in every circle!

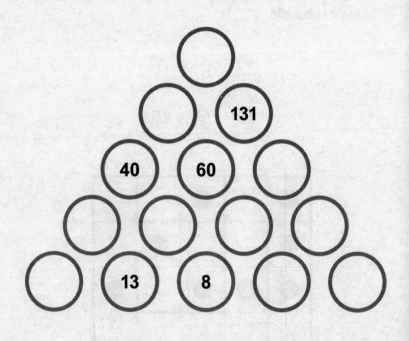

One to Nine

Using the numbers below, complete these six equations
(three reading across and three reading downwards).
Every number is used once.

1   2   3

4   5   6

7   8   9

	x	7	–		=	33
–		+		x		
	+		–		=	7
x		x		+		
	–		x		=	21
=		=		=		
8		16		15		

211

Number Crunch

Starting at the left with the number provided, work across from one box to another, applying the mathematical instructions to your running total.

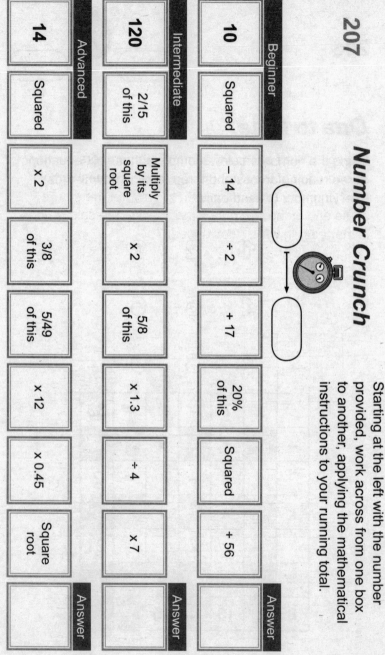

Beginner

| 10 | Squared | − 14 | ÷ 2 | + 17 | 20% of this | Squared | + 56 | Answer |

Intermediate

| 120 | 2/15 of this | Multiply by its square root | × 2 | 5/8 of this | × 1.3 | ÷ 4 | × 7 | Answer |

Advanced

| 14 | Squared | × 2 | 3/8 of this | 5/49 of this | × 12 | × 0.45 | Square root | Answer |

Summing Up

Arrange one of each of the four given numbers, as well as one each of the symbols – (minus), x (times) and + (plus) in every row and column to arrive at the answer at the end of the row or column, making the calculations in the order in which they appear.

1 6

7 8

7	–	1	+	6	x	8	=	96
x								
						=	97
			1			=	54
						=	9
=		=		=		=		
51		49		35		55		

Isolate

Draw walls to partition the grid into areas (some walls are already drawn in for you). Each area must contain two circles, area sizes must match those shown by the numbers next to the grid and each '+' must be linked to at least two walls.

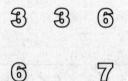

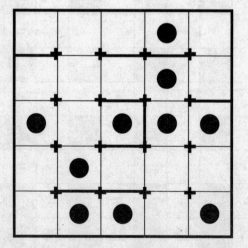

Pyramid Plus

The number in each circle is the sum of the two numbers below it. Just work out the missing numbers in every circle!

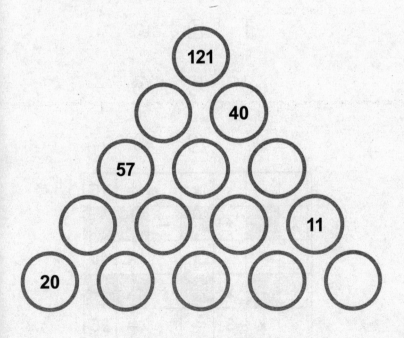

One to Nine

Using the numbers below, complete these six equations (three reading across and three reading downwards). Every number is used once.

	−		x		=	16
x		+		−		
	+		x		=	40
+		x		+		
	x	3	−		=	25
=		=		=		
15		33		5		

Number Crunch

Starting at the left with the number provided, work across from one box to another, applying the mathematical instructions to your running total.

Beginner							Answer
61	+ 5	÷ 11	× 13	2/3 of this	÷ 2	− 8	× 3	

Intermediate							Answer
329	− 24	÷ 5	+ 99	4/5 of this	× 3	5/6 of this	÷ 16	

Advanced							Answer
228	9/12 of this	5/9 of this	6/19 of this	Squared	27% of this	× 2	5/27 of this	

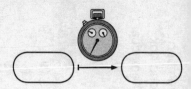

Summing Up

Arrange one of each of the four given numbers, as well as one each of the symbols – (minus), x (times) and + (plus) in every row and column to arrive at the answer at the end of the row or column, making the calculations in the order in which they appear.

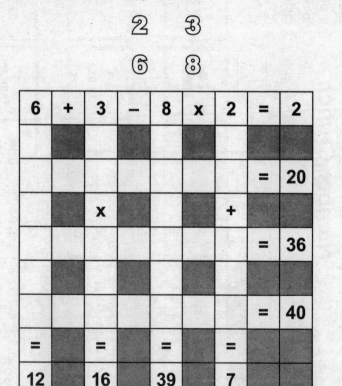

| 2 | 3 |
| 6 | 8 |

6	+	3	–	8	x	2	=	2
							=	20
		x				+		
							=	36
							=	40
=		=		=		=		
12		16		39		7		

218

Isolate

Draw walls to partition the grid into areas (some walls
are already drawn in for you). Each area must contain
two circles, area sizes must match those shown by the
numbers next to the grid and each '+' must be linked to
at least two walls.

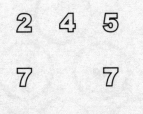

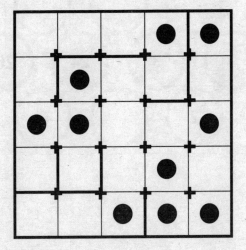

Pyramid Plus

The number in each circle is the sum of the two numbers below it. Just work out the missing numbers in every circle!

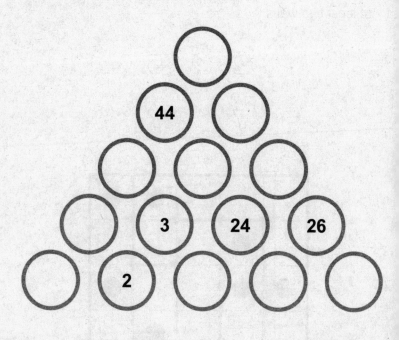

One to Nine

Using the numbers below, complete these six equations (three reading across and three reading downwards). Every number is used once.

1 2 3

4 5 6

7 8 9

	x		+		=	8
+		x		+		
	−		x	8	=	24
x		−		x		
	+		x		=	42
=		=		=		
28		2		77		

Number Crunch

Starting at the left with the number provided, work across from one box to another, applying the mathematical instructions to your running total.

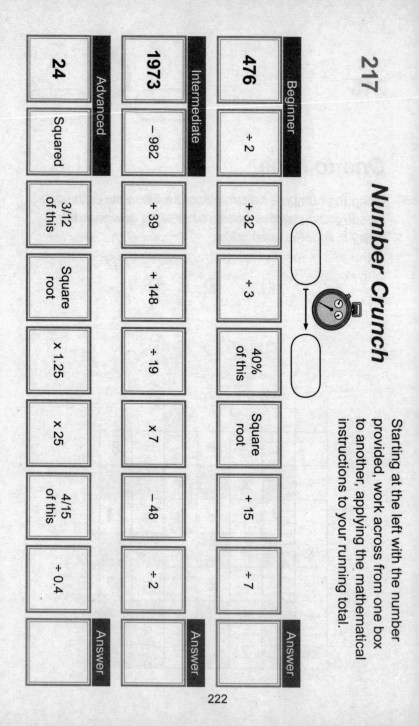

Beginner

| 476 | ÷ 2 | + 32 | ÷ 3 | 40% of this | Square root | + 15 | ÷ 7 | Answer |

Intermediate

| 1973 | − 982 | + 39 | + 148 | ÷ 19 | × 7 | − 48 | ÷ 2 | Answer |

Advanced

| 24 | Squared | 3/12 of this | Square root | × 1.25 | × 25 | 4/15 of this | ÷ 0.4 | Answer |

Summing Up

Arrange one of each of the four given numbers, as well as one each of the symbols – (minus), x (times) and + (plus) in every row and column to arrive at the answer at the end of the row or column, making the calculations in the order in which they appear.

3 4

5 9

3	+	5	x	4	–	9	=	23
		–						
						3	=	28
							=	38
				9			=	22
=		=		=		=		
40		12		26		34		

Isolate

Draw walls to partition the grid into areas (some walls are already drawn in for you). Each area must contain two circles, area sizes must match those shown by the numbers next to the grid and each '+' must be linked to at least two walls.

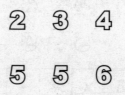

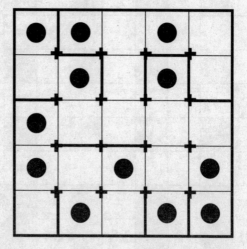

Pyramid Plus

The number in each circle is the sum of the two numbers below it. Just work out the missing numbers in every circle!

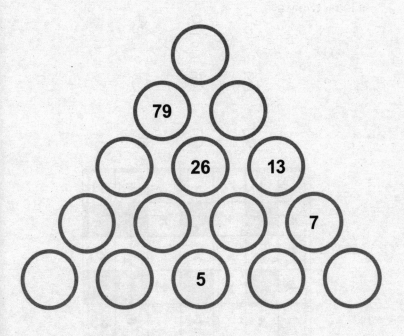

One to Nine

Using the numbers below, complete these six equations
(three reading across and three reading downwards).
Every number is used once.

1 2 3

4 5 6

7 8 9

	+		–		=	11
x		+		x		
7	–		x		=	25
–		x		+		
	x		–		=	35
=		=		=		
38		90		16		

Number Crunch

Starting at the left with the number provided, work across from one box to another, applying the mathematical instructions to your running total.

Beginner

| 522 | ÷ 9 | + 12 | 10% of this | × 5 | + 45 | × 1.05 | ÷ 12 | Answer |

Intermediate

| 41 | + 92 | × 4 | 3/4 of this | + 2/3 of this | + 85 | × 1.3 | − 489 | Answer |

Advanced

| 38 | × 16 | 3/8 of this | 5/19 of this | + 45% | + 2/3 of this | 27/29 of this | 11/15 of this | Answer |

Summing Up

Arrange one of each of the four given numbers, as well as one each of the symbols – (minus), x (times) and + (plus) in every row and column to arrive at the answer at the end of the row or column, making the calculations in the order in which they appear.

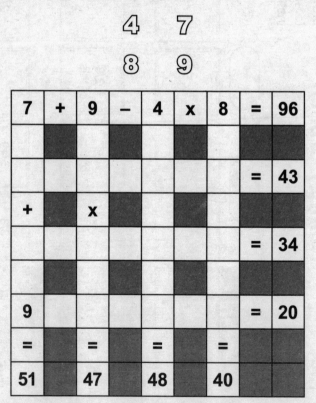

Isolate

Draw walls to partition the grid into areas (some walls are already drawn in for you). Each area must contain two circles, area sizes must match those shown by the numbers next to the grid and each '+' must be linked to at least two walls.

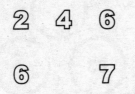

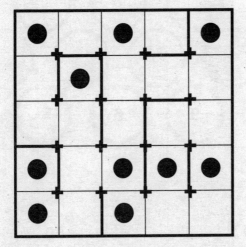

Pyramid Plus

The number in each circle is the sum of the two numbers below it. Just work out the missing numbers in every circle!

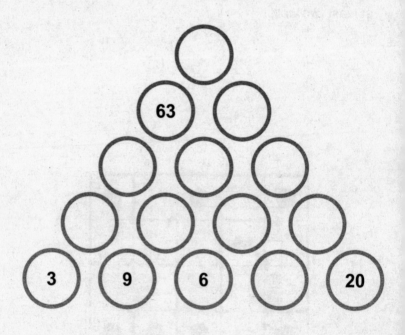

One to Nine

Using the numbers below, complete these six equations (three reading across and three reading downwards). Every number is used once.

1   2   3

4   5   6

7   8   9

6	**–**		**x**		**=**	**25**
+		**+**		**x**		
	x		**+**		**=**	**16**
x		**x**		**–**		
	+		**x**		**=**	**48**
=		**=**		**=**		
56		**45**		**37**		

Number Crunch

Starting at the left with the number provided, work across from one box to another, applying the mathematical instructions to your running total.

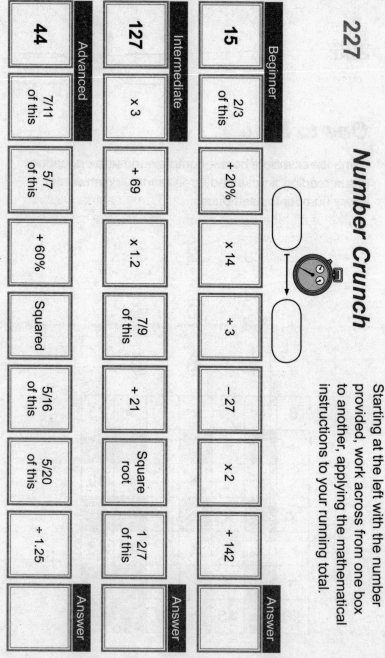

Beginner

| 15 | 2/3 of this | + 20% | × 14 | ÷ 3 | − 27 | × 2 | + 142 | Answer |

Intermediate

| 127 | × 3 | + 69 | × 1.2 | 7/9 of this | + 21 | Square root | 1 2/7 of this | Answer |

Advanced

| 44 | 7/11 of this | 5/7 of this | + 60% | Squared | 5/16 of this | 5/20 of this | ÷ 1.25 | Answer |

Summing Up

Arrange one of each of the four given numbers, as well
as one each of the symbols – (minus), x (times) and +
(plus) in every row and column to arrive at the answer
at the end of the row or column, making the calculations
in the order in which they appear.

6	–	1	+	7	x	4	=	48
	▓		▓		▓		▓	▓
							=	33
	▓		▓		▓		▓	▓
	–						=	19
	▓		▓		▓		▓	▓
		6	–				=	21
=	▓	=	▓	=	▓	=	▓	▓
15	▓	9	▓	44	▓	3	▓	▓

Isolate

Draw walls to partition the grid into areas (some walls are already drawn in for you). Each area must contain two circles, area sizes must match those shown by the numbers next to the grid and each '+' must be linked to at least two walls.

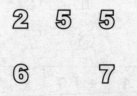

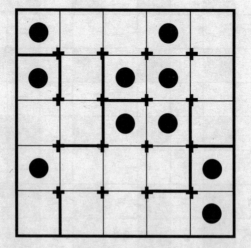

Pyramid Plus

The number in each circle is the sum of the two numbers below it. Just work out the missing numbers in every circle!

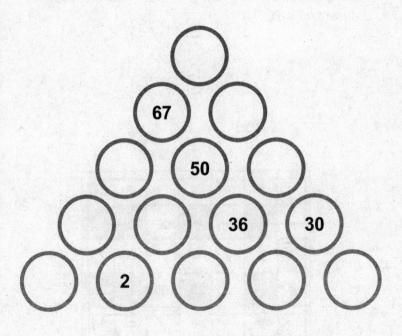

One to Nine

Using the numbers below, complete these six equations
(three reading across and three reading downwards).
Every number is used once.

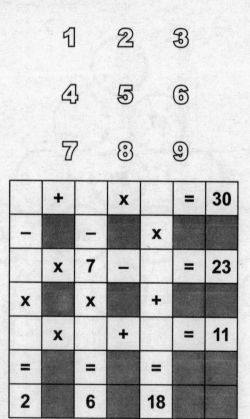

	+		x		=	30
−		−		x		
	x	7	−		=	23
x		x		+		
	x		+		=	11
=		=		=		
2		6		18		

Number Crunch

Starting at the left with the number provided, work across from one box to another, applying the mathematical instructions to your running total.

Beginner

| 250 | 50% of this | ÷ 5 | ×7 | × 2 | + 40 | × 1.2 | ÷ 9 | Answer |

Intermediate

| 49 | 6/7 of this | ÷ 3 | × 5 | ÷ 0.2 | 4/5 of this | ÷ 70 | Cubed | Answer |

Advanced

| 24 | ÷ 0.25 | 7/12 of this | × 1.875 | 19/21 of this | 7/19 of this | 1 5/7 of this | ÷ 1.25 | Answer |

237

Summing Up

Arrange one of each of the four given numbers, as well as one each of the symbols – (minus), x (times) and + (plus) in every row and column to arrive at the answer at the end of the row or column, making the calculations in the order in which they appear.

5	+	9	–	8	x	2	=	12
–								
							=	20
							=	48
						+		
				9			=	59
=		=		=		=		
35		83		17		15		

Isolate

Draw walls to partition the grid into areas (some walls are already drawn in for you). Each area must contain two circles, area sizes must match those shown by the numbers next to the grid and each '+' must be linked to at least two walls.

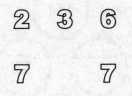

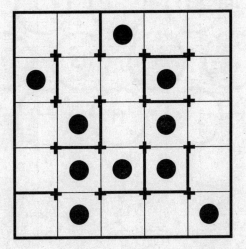

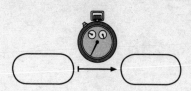

Pyramid Plus

The number in each circle is the sum of the two numbers below it. Just work out the missing numbers in every circle!

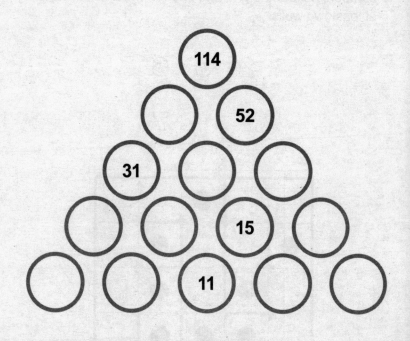

One to Nine

Using the numbers below, complete these six equations
(three reading across and three reading downwards).
Every number is used once.

	–		x		=	4
–		x		+		
	x		+	6	=	30
x		–		x		
	–		x		=	20
=		=		=		
42		38		28		

241

237

Number Crunch

Starting at the left with the number provided, work across from one box to another, applying the mathematical instructions to your running total.

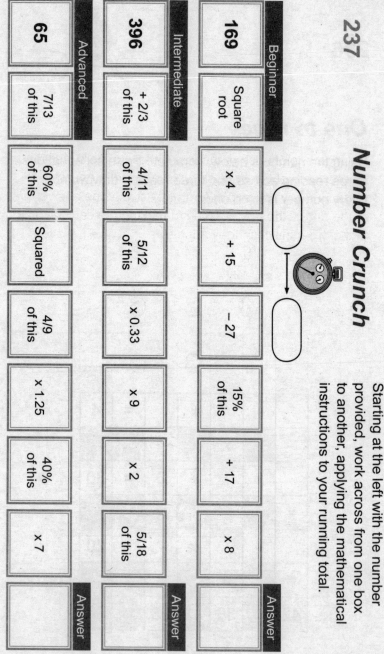

Beginner							
169	Square root	× 4	+ 15	− 27	15% of this	+ 17	× 8	Answer

Intermediate							
396	+ 2/3 of this	4/11 of this	5/12 of this	× 0.33	× 9	× 2	5/18 of this	Answer

Advanced							
65	7/13 of this	60% of this	Squared	4/9 of this	× 1.25	40% of this	× 7	Answer

242

Summing Up

Arrange one of each of the four given numbers, as well as one each of the symbols – (minus), x (times) and + (plus) in every row and column to arrive at the answer at the end of the row or column, making the calculations in the order in which they appear.

3 4

5 8

4	+	8	–	3	x	5	=	45
x								
							=	11
						8	=	19
						x		
							=	29
=		=		=		=		
25		23		39		40		

Isolate

Draw walls to partition the grid into areas (some walls are already drawn in for you). Each area must contain two circles, area sizes must match those shown by the numbers next to the grid and each '+' must be linked to at least two walls.

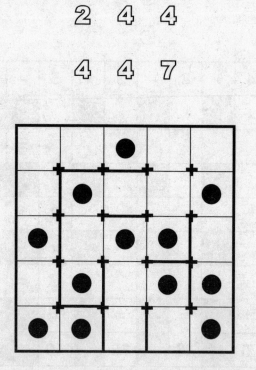

Pyramid Plus

The number in each circle is the sum of the two numbers below it. Just work out the missing numbers in every circle!

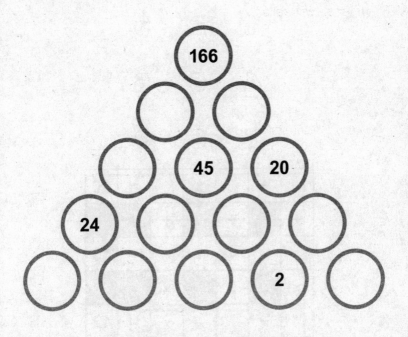

One to Nine

Using the numbers below, complete these six equations
(three reading across and three reading downwards).
Every number is used once.

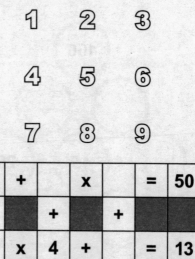

	+		x		=	50
+		+		+		
	x	4	+		=	13
x		x		x		
	+		–		=	12
=		=		=		
24		88		28		

242

Number Crunch

Starting at the left with the number provided, work across from one box to another, applying the mathematical instructions to your running total.

Beginner

196	1/4 of this	Square root of this	+ 28	× 3	+ 29	Half of this	+ 27	Answer

Intermediate

39	× 5	2/3 of this	× 1.6	3/4 of this	+ 92	× 3	+ 146	Answer

Advanced

72	× 18	3/8 of this	7/18 of this	+ 83	14/17 of this	12.5% of this	÷ 0.2	Answer

247

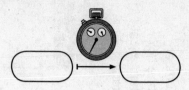

Summing Up

Arrange one of each of the four given numbers, as well as one each of the symbols – (minus), x (times) and + (plus) in every row and column to arrive at the answer at the end of the row or column, making the calculations in the order in which they appear.

8	–	4	+	7	x	5	=	55
				–				
							=	40
							=	39
					x		=	49
=		=		=		=		
25		31		29		63		

244

Isolate

Draw walls to partition the grid into areas (some walls are already drawn in for you). Each area must contain two circles, area sizes must match those shown by the numbers next to the grid and each '+' must be linked to at least two walls.

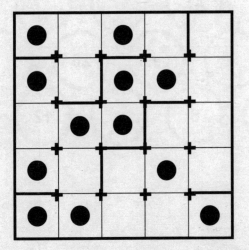

Pyramid Plus

The number in each circle is the sum of the two numbers below it. Just work out the missing numbers in every circle!

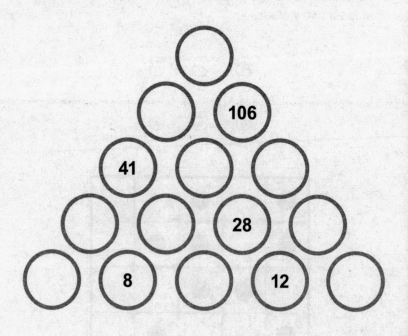

One to Nine

Using the numbers below, complete these six equations (three reading across and three reading downwards). Every number is used once.

	+		−		=	6
x		−		+		
	x		+		=	8
+		x		−		
9	−		x		=	4
=		=		=		
13		21		7		

Number Crunch

Starting at the left with the number provided, work across from one box to another, applying the mathematical instructions to your running total.

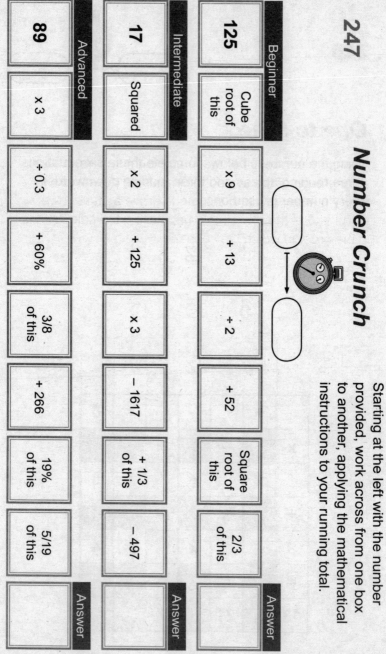

Beginner

| 125 | Cube root of this | × 9 | + 13 | ÷ 2 | + 52 | Square root of this | 2/3 of this | Answer |

Intermediate

| 17 | Squared | × 2 | + 125 | × 3 | − 1617 | + 1/3 of this | − 497 | Answer |

Advanced

| 89 | × 3 | + 0.3 | + 60% | 3/8 of this | + 266 | 19% of this | 5/19 of this | Answer |

Summing Up

Arrange one of each of the four given numbers, as well as one each of the symbols – (minus), x (times) and + (plus) in every row and column to arrive at the answer at the end of the row or column, making the calculations in the order in which they appear.

2 3

4 9

9	–	2	+	4	x	3	=	33
							=	61
		+		x				
							=	19
						9	=	27
=		=		=		=		
20		14		37		45		

Isolate

Draw walls to partition the grid into areas (some walls are already drawn in for you). Each area must contain two circles, area sizes must match those shown by the numbers next to the grid and each '+' must be linked to at least two walls.

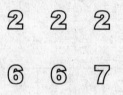

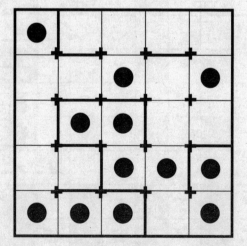

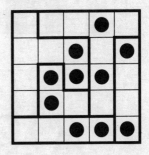

1

4	x	6	–	9	=	15
+		x		+		
8	–	1	x	3	=	21
–		+		x		
2	x	5	+	7	=	17
=		=		=		
10		11		84		

2

Beginner:
94 – 16 = 78, 78 ÷ 2 = 39, 39 ÷ 3 x 2 = 26, 26 + 14 = 40, 40 ÷ 5 x 3 = 24, 24 x 3 = 72, 72 + 28 = 100

Intermediate:
2222 ÷ 11 = 202, 150% of 202 = 303, 303 + 30 = 333, 333 ÷ 37 x 5 = 45, 45 ÷ 15 = 3, 3 ÷ 3 x 2 = 2, 2 x 86 = 172

Advanced:
247 ÷ 13 x 3 = 57, 57 ÷ 19 x 5 = 15, 15 x 35 = 525, 525 ÷ 21 x 5 = 125, cube root of 125 = 5, 5 x 1.4 = 7, 7 x 45 = 315

3

3	+	8	x	2	–	7	=	15
–		–		+		+		
2	+	7	–	3	x	8	=	48
+		+		x		x		
7	–	3	+	8	x	2	=	24
x		x		–		–		
8	x	2	–	7	+	3	=	12
=		=		=		=		
64		8		33		27		

4

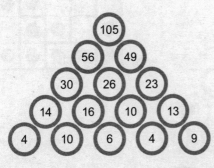

5

```
          105
       56    49
     30   26   23
   14   16   10   13
  4   10   6   4   9
```

255

6

8	–	1	x	5	=	35
+		+		x		
2	x	9	+	3	=	21
–		x		+		
4	x	6	–	7	=	17
=		=		=		
6		60		22		

7

Beginner:
$47 - 38 = 9$, $9^2 = 81$, $81 \div 3 = 27$, $27 + 9 = 36$, square root of $36 = 6$, $6 \times 7 = 42$, $42 - 18 = 24$

Intermediate:
$55 \div 11 \times 4 = 20$, $20 \times 1.75 = 35$, $35 \div 7 \times 2 = 10$, 400% of $10 = 40$, $40 + 47 = 87$, $87 \div 3 \times 2 = 58$, $58 \div 0.5 = 116$

Advanced:
$33 \times 25 = 825$, $825 \div 3 \times 2 = 550$, $550 \div 11 \times 9 = 450$, 28% of $450 = 126$, $126 \div 14 \times 5 = 45$, $45 + 89 = 134$, $134 \div 0.25 = 536$

8

5	+	9	x	3	–	6	=	36
–		x		x		+		
3	x	5	–	6	+	9	=	18
x		–		+		x		
9	+	6	x	5	–	3	=	72
+		+		–		–		
6	–	3	x	9	+	5	=	32
=		=		=		=		
24		42		14		40		

9

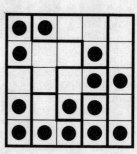

10

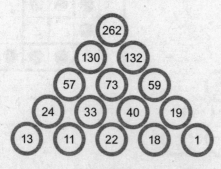

11

2	+	7	−	5	=	4
+		−		x		
6	x	3	−	8	=	10
x		+		−		
9	−	1	x	4	=	32
=		=		=		
72		5		36		

12

Beginner:
$6 \div 3 = 2$, $2^2 = 4$, $4 \times 8 = 32$, $32 \div 8 \times 3 = 12$, $12 + 98 = 110$, 10% of $110 = 11$, $11 \times 12 = 132$

Intermediate:
$59 \times 3 = 177$, $177 - 114 = 63$, $63 + 21 = 84$, $84 \div 12 \times 5 = 35$, $35 \div 7 \times 3 = 15$, $15 \times 13 = 195$, $195 + 85 = 280$

Advanced:
$578 \div 2 = 289$, square root of $289 = 17$, $17 + 68 = 85$, 80% of $85 = 68$, $68 \times 1.75 = 119$, $119 \times 2 = 238$, $238 - 109 = 129$

13

6	x	9	−	4	+	7	=	57
−		+		x		−		
4	+	7	−	9	x	6	=	12
x		−		−		x		
7	−	4	x	6	+	9	=	27
+		x		+		+		
9	+	6	−	7	x	4	=	32
=		=		=		=		
23		72		37		13		

14

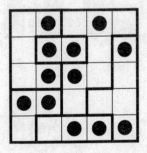

15

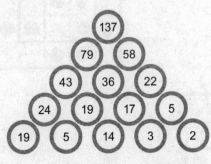

16

5	+	4	x	7	=	63
–		x		+		
3	x	9	–	1	=	26
x		+		x		
2	x	6	+	8	=	20
=		=		=		
4		42		64		

17

Beginner:
$51 \div 3 = 17$, $17 + 18 = 35$, $35 \div 5 \times 4 = 28$, $28 \div 4 \times 3 = 21$, $21 + 37 = 58$, $58 - 49 = 9$, $9 \times 8 = 72$
Intermediate:
$32 \times 5 = 160$, $160 + 16 = 176$, $176 \div 4 = 44$, $44 \div 11 \times 5 = 20$, $20 \times 4.5 = 90$, $90 \div 5 = 18$, $18 \times 3 = 54$
Advanced:
$240 \div 40 \times 9 = 54$, $54 \times 7 = 378$, $378 \div 18 \times 11 = 231$, $231 \div 1.5 = 154$, $154 \times 5 = 770$, $770 \times 1.6 = 1232$, $1232 + 2321 = 3553$

18

2	+	8	x	5	–	4	=	46
x		–		–		+		
5	x	4	–	2	+	8	=	26
–		+		x		x		
4	+	2	x	8	–	5	=	43
+		x		+		–		
8	x	5	+	4	–	2	=	42
=		=		=		=		
14		30		28		58		

19

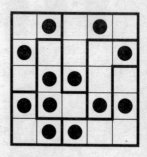

20

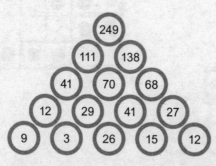

258

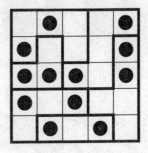

21

8	x	3	+	6	=	30
–		+		x		
5	+	2	x	7	=	49
+		x		–		
1	+	9	x	4	=	40
=		=		=		
4		45		38		

22

Beginner:
$10 \div 5 \times 2 = 4$, $4^2 = 16$, $16 \div 4 \times 3 = 12$, $12 \times 9 = 108$, $108 \div 6 = 18$, $18 + 48 = 66$, $66 \div 3 = 22$
Intermediate:
$99 \div 9 \times 5 = 55$, $55 \div 11 \times 5 = 25$, square root of $25 = 5$, $5 + 1 = 6$, $6 + 5 = 11$, $11^2 = 121$, $121 \times 3 = 363$
Advanced:
$161 \div 7 \times 4 = 92$, $92 + 749 = 841$, $841 \times 3 = 2523$, $2523 + 1682 = 4205$, $4205 \div 5 = 841$, $841 + 92 = 933$, $933 - 719 = 214$

23

3	+	7	–	9	x	6	=	6
x		–		+		x		
9	–	3	x	6	+	7	=	43
+		x		–		–		
6	x	9	+	7	–	3	=	58
–		+		x		+		
7	–	6	+	3	x	9	=	36
=		=		=		=		
26		42		24		48		

24

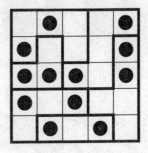

25

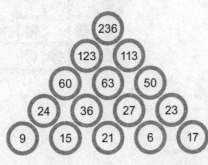

26

4	+	2	x	5	=	30
+		x		−		
6	+	9	−	3	=	12
−		+		x		
8	−	1	x	7	=	49
=		=		=		
2		19		14		

27

Beginner:
$56 + 15 = 71$, $71 - 7 = 64$, $64 \div 4 = 16$, square root of 16 = 4, $4 + 69 = 73$, $73 - 14 = 59$, $59 + 23 = 82$

Intermediate:
$127 + 43 = 170$, $170 + 34 = 204$, $204 \div 4 = 51$, $51 \div 3 = 17$, $17 + 283 = 300$, 31% of 300 = 93, $93 - 67 = 26$

Advanced:
$76^2 = 5776$, $5776 \div 8 \times 5 = 3610$, $3610 \div 10 \times 7 = 2527$, $2527 \div 7 \times 2 = 722$, $722 + 82 = 804$, $804 \div 4 \times 3 = 603$, $603 \div 9 \times 7 = 469$

28

6	+	4	x	8	−	3	=	77
−		+		−		x		
3	x	8	−	4	+	6	=	26
x		x		x		+		
4	−	3	x	6	+	8	=	14
+		−		+		−		
8	+	6	−	3	x	4	=	44
=		=		=		=		
20		30		27		22		

29

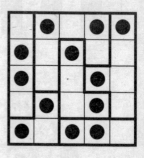

30

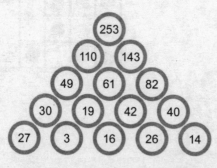

260

31

8	–	6	x	4	=	8
+		x		+		
1	+	3	x	9	=	36
x		+		x		
5	x	7	–	2	=	33
=		=		=		
45		25		26		

32

Beginner:
90 ÷ 5 = 18, 18 ÷ 3 x 2 = 12, 12 ÷ 4 x 3 = 9, 9 x 8 = 72, 72 + 28 = 100, 100 + 20 = 120, 120 ÷ 3 = 40

Intermediate:
32 ÷ 8 x 7 = 28, 125% of 28 = 35, 35 x 7 = 245, 245 + 27 = 272, 272 ÷ 4 = 68, 68 ÷ 4 = 17, 17 + 84 = 101

Advanced:
5 x 5 x 9 = 225, square root of 225 = 15, 15 x 39 = 585, 585 ÷ 9 x 4 + 585 = 845, 845 ÷ 5 = 169, 169 – 77 = 92, 92 x 3 + (92 ÷ 4 x 3) = 345

33

5	+	9	x	2	–	7	=	21
–		–		+		+		
2	x	5	–	7	+	9	=	12
+		x		x		x		
7	–	2	x	9	+	5	=	50
x		+		–		–		
9	+	7	–	5	x	2	=	22
=		=		=		=		
90		15		76		78		

34

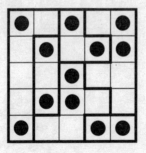

35

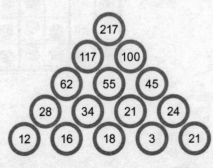

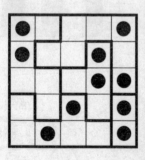

36

9	−	3	x	8	=	48
+		x		−		
2	+	6	x	5	=	40
x		−		x		
7	+	4	−	1	=	10
=		=		=		
77		14		3		

37

Beginner:
1001 x 5 = 5005, 5005 − 355 = 4650, 10% of 4650 = 465, 465 ÷ 5 = 93, 93 ÷ 3 = 31, 31 + 29 = 60, 60 ÷ 4 = 15

Intermediate:
19 x 4 = 76, 76 − 18 = 58, 58 + 37 = 95, 95 ÷ 19 x 16 = 80, 20% of 80 = 16, square root of 16 = 4, 4 x 23 = 92

Advanced:
425 ÷ 17 x 11 = 275, 275 ÷ 11 x 5 = 125, 125 x 0.4 = 50, 320% of 50 = 160, 160 ÷ 32 x 23 = 115, 115 ÷ 23 x 18 = 90, 90 ÷ 0.3 = 300

38

4	+	7	x	3	−	8	=	25
x		−		+		−		
8	−	3	x	7	+	4	=	39
−		x		x		+		
3	x	4	−	8	+	7	=	11
+		+		−		x		
7	x	8	+	4	−	3	=	57
=		=		=		=		
36		24		76		33		

39

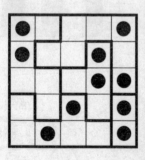

40

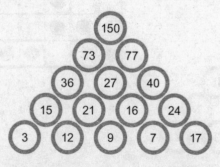

41

4	+	1	x	7	=	35
x		+		−		
6	+	8	−	2	=	12
−		x		+		
3	x	5	+	9	=	24
=		=		=		
21		45		14		

42

Beginner:
31 − 15 = 16, 16 + 4 = 20, 20 + 18 = 38, 38 ÷ 2 = 19, 19 − 11 = 8, 8^2 = 64, 64 + 146 = 210

Intermediate:
1215 ÷ 5 = 243, 243 ÷ 27 = 9, 9 ÷ 9 x 5 + 9 = 14, 14 ÷ 7 x 3 = 6, 6 + 4 = 10, 950% of 10 = 95, 95 + 36 = 131

Advanced:
36 + 20 = 56, 56 x 1.375 = 77, 77 x 7 = 539, 539 − 33 = 506, 506 ÷ 22 x 19 = 437, 437 − 91 = 346, 346 x 2.5 = 865

43

5	x	8	+	2	−	6	=	36
+		−		x		+		
6	−	2	x	5	+	8	=	28
x		+		−		x		
8	−	5	+	6	x	2	=	18
−		x		+		−		
2	+	6	x	8	−	5	=	59
=		=		=		=		
86		66		12		23		

44

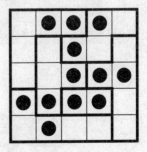

45

46

3	x	6	–	9	=	9
+		–		+		
2	+	5	x	7	=	49
x		x		x		
8	–	1	+	4	=	11
=		=		=		
40		1		64		

48

5	+	7	–	2	x	9	=	90
–		+		x		–		
2	x	5	+	9	–	7	=	12
x		x		–		+		
9	–	2	x	7	+	5	=	54
+		–		+		x		
7	+	9	x	5	–	2	=	78
=		=		=		=		
34		15		16		14		

47

Beginner:
60% of 200 = 120, 120 ÷ 4 = 30, 30 + 10 = 40, 40 x 4 = 160, 160 ÷ 20 = 8, 8 x 11 = 88, 88 – 42 = 46

Intermediate:
488 ÷ 8 = 61, 61 – 17 = 44, 44 ÷ 11 x 5 + 44 = 64, cube root of 64 = 4, 4 x 26 = 104, 104 ÷ 4 x 3 = 78, 78 ÷ 3 = 26

Advanced:
92 ÷ 23 x 17 = 68, 68 ÷ 17 x 4 = 16, 16^2 = 256, 256 x 0.375 = 96, 96 ÷ 16 x 3 = 18, 18^2 = 324, 324 ÷ 36 x 23 = 207

49

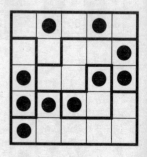

50

264

51

3	+	7	x	1	=	10
x		–		+		
6	–	5	x	9	=	9
+		x		x		
8	x	4	+	2	=	34
=		=		=		
26		8		20		

52

Beginner:
95 + 18 = 113, 113 – 72 = 41,
41 x 2 = 82, 82 x 1.5 = 123, 123
– 16 = 107, 107 – 17 = 90, 90 x
4 = 360
Intermediate:
49 x 2 = 98, 98 – 19 = 79, 79 x
3 = 237, 237 – 109 = 128, 128
÷ 8 = 16, 16 x 1.5 = 24, 24 ÷ 8
x 5 = 15
Advanced:
59 x 4 = 236, 236 ÷ 4 x 3 + 236
= 413, 413 – 78 = 335, 335 x
0.2 = 67, 67 + 233 = 300, 61%
of 300 = 183, 183 ÷ 3 x 2 + 183
= 305

53

5	–	3	+	8	x	7	=	70
+		x		–		+		
8	+	7	–	5	x	3	=	30
x		–		x		–		
3	x	8	+	7	–	5	=	26
–		+		+		x		
7	–	5	x	3	+	8	=	14
=		=		=		=		
32		18		24		40		

54

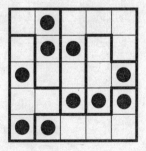

55

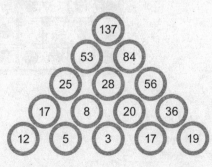

56

4	x	9	–	6	=	30
x		+		–		
3	+	7	x	1	=	10
+		–		+		
8	–	5	x	2	=	6
=		=		=		
20		11		7		

57

Beginner:
$2^2 = 4$, 4 x 9 = 36, square root of 36 = 6, 6 x 7 = 42, 42 ÷ 3 = 14, 14 + 8 = 22, 22 + 38 = 60
Intermediate:
291 + 49 = 340, 20% of 340 = 68, 68 ÷ 4 = 17, 17 x 7 = 119, 119 x 2 = 238, 238 – 190 = 48, 48 ÷ 3 x 2 + 48 = 80
Advanced:
72 ÷ 12 x 7 = 42, 300% of 42 = 126, 126 ÷ 14 x 11 = 99, 99 ÷ 0.3 = 330, 330 ÷ 11 x 10 = 300, 94% of 300 = 282, 282 ÷ 3 x 2 = 188

58

9	–	3	+	1	x	8	=	56
+		x		+		–		
1	x	9	–	8	+	3	=	4
x		–		x		+		
3	+	8	x	9	–	1	=	98
–		+		–		x		
8	–	1	+	3	x	9	=	90
=		=		=		=		
22		20		78		54		

59

60

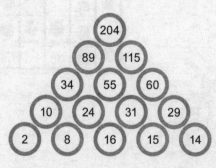

266

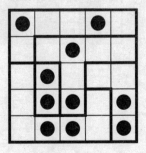

61

9	–	2	+	7	=	14
–		+		–		
4	+	8	–	3	=	9
x		x		+		
1	x	6	+	5	=	11
=		=		=		
5		60		9		

62

Beginner:
35 ÷ 5 = 7, 7 + 27 = 34, 34 x 2 = 68, 68 ÷ 4 = 17, 17 – 8 = 9, square root of 9 = 3, 3 x 15 = 45

Intermediate:
29 – 14 = 15, 15^2 = 225, 225 ÷ 3 = 75, 75 ÷ 3 x 2 + 75 = 125, 125 ÷ 5 x 4 = 100, 67% of 100 = 67, 67 + 88 = 155

Advanced:
43 x 7 = 301, 301 + 199 = 500, 69% of 500 = 345, 345 ÷ 15 x 9 = 207, 207 ÷ 23 x 17 = 153, 153 ÷ 9 x 4 = 68, 68 x 7 = 476

63

3	x	7	–	5	+	2	=	18
+		–		x		+		
5	–	2	x	7	+	3	=	24
x		x		–		x		
2	+	5	x	3	–	7	=	14
–		+		+		–		
7	+	3	x	2	–	5	=	15
=		=		=		=		
9		28		34		30		

64

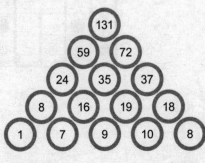

65

- 131
- 59, 72
- 24, 35, 37
- 8, 16, 19, 18
- 1, 7, 9, 10, 8

66

4	x	3	–	7	=	5
+		x		+		
1	x	6	+	9	=	15
x		+		–		
8	–	5	x	2	=	6
=		=		=		
40		23		14		

67

Beginner:
$67 - 22 = 45$, $45 \div 9 = 5$, $5^2 = 25$, $25 \times 5 = 125$, $125 + 25 = 150$, 10% of $150 = 15$, $15 + 29 = 44$

Intermediate:
9% of $700 = 63$, $63 - 28 = 35$, $35 \times 4 = 140$, $140 + 42 = 182$, $182 \div 2 = 91$, $91 - 17 = 74$, $74 + 123 = 197$

Advanced:
$171 \div 9 = 19$, $19^2 = 361$, $361 - 59 = 302$, $302 \times 2.5 = 755$, $7 \times 5 \times 5 = 175$, $175 \div 7 \times 3 = 75$, $75 \div 0.75 = 100$

68

9	–	3	+	4	x	7	=	70
x		+		+		–		
4	+	7	x	9	–	3	=	96
–		x		–		x		
7	x	9	–	3	+	4	=	64
+		–		x		+		
3	+	4	x	7	–	9	=	40
=		=		=		=		
32		86		70		25		

70

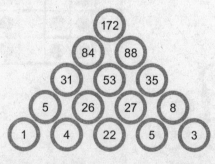

69

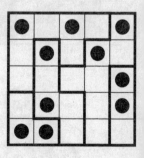

268

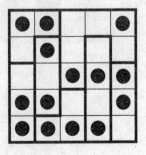

71

2	x	5	–	9	=	1
+		x		–		
7	x	1	+	3	=	10
–		+		x		
6	+	4	x	8	=	80
=		=		=		
3		9		48		

72

Beginner:
9 + 14 = 23, 23 x 2 = 46, 46 – 19 = 27, 27 ÷ 3 x 2 = 18, 18 ÷ 9 = 2, 2 + 1 = 3, 3 x 7 = 21

Intermediate:
829 – 555 = 274, 274 ÷ 2 = 137, 137 + 85 = 222, 222 ÷ 37 = 6, 6^3 = 216, 216 ÷ 9 x 3 = 72, 72 ÷ 8 x 3 = 27

Advanced:
256 ÷ 0.5 = 512, cube root of 512 = 8, 8 x 1.75 = 14, 14 x 2.5 = 35, 35^2 = 1225, 1225 ÷ 49 x 6 = 150, 68% of 150 = 102

73

4	+	3	x	9	–	6	=	57
x		+		–		+		
6	–	4	+	3	x	9	=	45
–		x		+		x		
9	–	6	x	4	+	3	=	15
+		–		x		–		
3	x	9	–	6	+	4	=	25
=		=		=		=		
18		33		60		41		

74

75

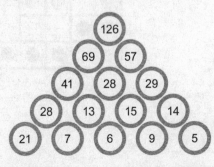

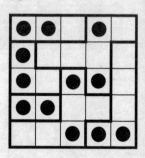

76

9	−	1	+	4	=	12
−		+		x		
3	+	7	x	5	=	50
+		x		−		
2	x	6	+	8	=	20
=		=		=		
8		48		12		

77

Beginner:
$12^2 = 144$, $144 ÷ 3 = 48$, $48 ÷ 6 = 8$, $8 \times 5 = 40$, $40 \times 1.5 = 60$, $60 ÷ 5 = 12$, $12 \times 11 = 132$

Intermediate:
$23 \times 11 = 253$, $253 − 192 = 61$, $61 \times 4 = 244$, $244 + 62 = 306$, $306 ÷ 3 = 102$, $102 ÷ 6 \times 5 = 85$, $85 + 97 = 182$

Advanced:
$156 + 35 = 191$, $191 \times 3 = 573$, $573 + 382 = 955$, $955 − 151 = 804$, $804 + 536 = 1340$, $1340 ÷ 20 \times 7 = 469$, $469 ÷ 7 \times 4 = 268$

78

7	+	3	x	8	−	2	=	78
−		x		+		+		
2	x	8	−	7	+	3	=	12
x		−		x		x		
3	+	7	−	2	x	8	=	64
+		+		−		−		
8	−	2	x	3	+	7	=	25
=		=		=		=		
23		19		27		33		

79

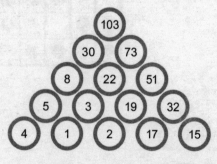

80

103
30 73
8 22 51
5 3 19 32
4 1 2 17 15

270

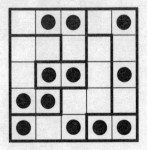

81

4	–	2	x	8	=	16
+		x		–		
7	+	5	x	1	=	12
–		+		x		
3	x	9	–	6	=	21
=		=		=		
8		19		42		

82

Beginner:
85 ÷ 5 = 17, 17 x 2 = 34, 34 + 8 = 42, 42 x 2 = 84, 84 ÷ 7 = 12, 12 + 88 = 100, 24% of 100 = 24
Intermediate:
456 ÷ 3 x 2 = 304, 304 ÷ 4 = 76, 76 x 1.5 = 114, 114 x 3 = 342, 342 ÷ 9 x 5 = 190, 190 – 19 = 171, 171 ÷ 19 x 2 = 18
Advanced:
285 ÷ 19 x 15 = 225, square root of 225 = 15, 15 ÷ 0.75 = 20, 20 x 23 = 460, 460 + 92 = 552, 552 + 184 = 736, 736 x 0.875 = 644

83

4	+	6	–	1	x	9	=	81
–		x		+		–		
1	x	9	+	6	–	4	=	11
x		+		x		+		
6	–	4	x	9	+	1	=	19
+		–		–		x		
9	+	1	x	4	–	6	=	34
=		=		=		=		
27		57		59		36		

84

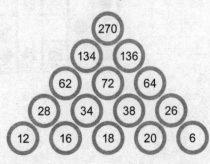

85

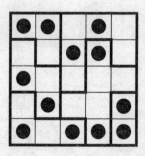

86

1	x	7	+	4	=	11
+		+		x		
5	x	9	−	3	=	42
−		x		+		
2	+	6	x	8	=	64
=		=		=		
4		96		20		

87

Beginner:
2006 − 1008 = 998, 998 ÷ 2 = 499, 499 − 9 = 490, 490 ÷ 70 = 7, 7 x 3 = 21, 21 + 8 = 29, 29 x 2 = 58

Intermediate:
340 ÷ 17 = 20, 20 x 2.5 = 50, 50^2 = 2500, 20% of 2500 = 500, 15% of 500 = 75, 75 x 9 = 675, 675 ÷ 3 x 2 = 450

Advanced:
234 ÷ 13 x 10 = 180, 180 − 169 = 11, 11^2 = 121, 121 + 683 = 804, 804 ÷ 0.4 = 2010, 2010 ÷ 67 x 2 = 60, 60 ÷ 1.25 = 48

88

3	+	8	−	7	x	5	=	20
x		−		x		+		
5	x	7	+	8	−	3	=	40
+		x		−		x		
7	+	3	x	5	−	8	=	42
−		+		+		−		
8	−	5	x	3	+	7	=	16
=		=		=		=		
14		8		54		57		

89

90

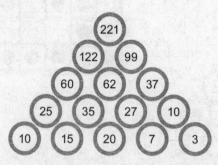

91

9	−	2	x	5	=	35
x		+		−		
4	+	7	x	1	=	11
−		x		x		
3	x	8	−	6	=	18
=		=		=		
33		72		24		

92

Beginner:
19 − 11 = 8, 8 x 4 = 32, 32 x 3 = 96, 96 − 18 = 78, 78 + 3 = 81, 81 ÷ 9 = 9, square root of 9 = 3
Intermediate:
73 − 37 = 36, square root of 36 = 6, 6 x 13 = 78, 78 ÷ 3 = 26, 26 ÷ 13 x 6 = 12, 12 ÷ 6 x 5 + 12 = 22, 22 x 11 = 242
Advanced:
91 x 11 = 1001, 1001 − 869 = 132, 132 ÷ 6 x 5 = 110, 110 + 33 = 143, 143 ÷ 0.25 = 572, 572 + 38 = 610, 80% of 610 = 488

93

9	−	4	x	7	+	6	=	41
+		x		−		x		
6	+	9	x	4	−	7	=	53
−		−		+		−		
4	x	7	−	6	+	9	=	31
x		+		x		+		
7	−	6	+	9	x	4	=	40
=		=		=		=		
77		35		81		35		

94

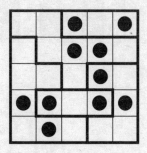

95

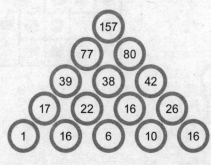

1	+	4	x	9	=	45
x		+		-		
7	x	6	-	2	=	40
+		x		+		
5	-	3	+	8	=	10
=		=		=		
12		30		15		

97

Beginner:
30 x 5 = 150, 150 ÷ 25 = 6, 6 x 9 = 54, 54 ÷ 2 = 27, 27 + 18 = 45, 45 x 2 = 90, 20% of 90 = 18
Intermediate:
35 + 53 = 88, 88 ÷ 8 x 5 = 55, 55 x 3 = 165, 165 ÷ 15 = 11, 300% of 11 = 33, 33 + 22 = 55, 55 ÷ 11 x 5 = 25
Advanced:
357 + 753 = 1110, 1110 ÷ 10 x 7 = 777, 777 + 518 = 1295, 1295 ÷ 5 = 259, 259 − 193 = 66, 66 + 86 = 152, 152 ÷ 19 x 17 = 136

98

6	x	2	+	5	-	8	=	9
+		x		-		-		
8	-	5	x	2	+	6	=	12
-		+		x		+		
5	+	6	x	8	-	2	=	86
x		-		+		x		
2	x	8	-	6	+	5	=	15
=		=		=		=		
18		8		30		20		

100

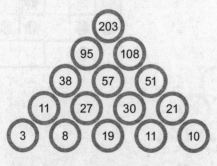

99

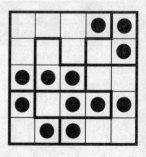

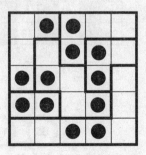

101

4	+	7	x	2	=	22
–		+		x		
1	x	6	+	8	=	14
x		–		+		
5	+	9	–	3	=	11
=		=		=		
15		4		19		

102

Beginner:
23 + 18 = 41, 41 x 3 = 123, 123 – 84 = 39, 39 ÷ 3 x 2 = 26, 26 ÷ 2 = 13, 13 + 19 = 32, 32 ÷ 4 x 3 = 24

Intermediate:
69 x 2 = 138, 138 ÷ 3 x 2 = 92, 92 ÷ 4 = 23, 23 + 137 = 160, 160 ÷ 5 x 2 = 64, square root of 64 = 8, cube root of 8 = 2

Advanced:
52 x 3 = 156, 156 x 1.25 = 195, 195 ÷ 13 x 7 = 105, 105 ÷ 7 x 5 = 75, 75 x 13 = 975, 975 ÷ 39 x 28 = 700, 39% of 700 = 273

103

9	–	3	+	7	x	4	=	52
+		x		+		–		
7	x	4	–	9	+	3	=	22
x		–		x		x		
4	+	7	x	3	–	9	=	24
–		+		–		+		
3	x	9	–	4	+	7	=	30
=		=		=		=		
61		14		44		16		

104

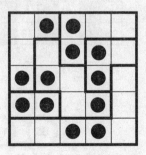

105

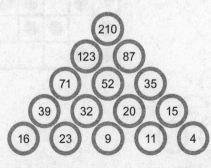

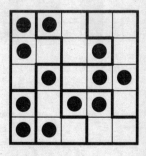

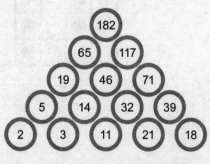

106

8	−	4	x	1	=	4
−		x		+		
3	+	9	−	7	=	5
+		−		x		
6	x	2	+	5	=	17
=		=		=		
11		34		40		

107

Beginner:
7 x 9 = 63, 63 − 45 = 18, 18 + 6 = 24, 24 ÷ 4 = 6, 6 x 5 = 30, 30 x 3 = 90, 30% of 90 = 27

Intermediate:
90 x 1.5 = 135, 135 ÷ 15 x 4 = 36, square root of 36 = 6, 6 x 2 + (6 ÷ 3) = 14, 14 + 49 = 63, 63 − 47 = 16, 16 x 2.5 = 40

Advanced:
162 ÷ 18 x 4 = 36, 36² = 1296, 1296 ÷ 72 = 18, 18 x 5 = 90, 90 ÷ 0.6 = 150, 150 ÷ 0.75 = 200, 30.5% of 200 = 61

108

8	+	2	x	5	−	7	=	43
−		x		−		+		
5	x	7	−	2	+	8	=	41
x		−		+		x		
7	−	5	x	8	+	2	=	18
+		+		x		−		
2	+	8	x	7	−	5	=	65
=		=		=		=		
23		17		77		25		

109

110

276

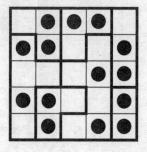

111

8	−	4	x	1	=	4
−		+		x		
3	x	6	−	9	=	9
x		x		−		
7	+	5	x	2	=	24
=		=		=		
35		50		7		

112

Beginner:
17 x 2 = 34, 34 + 28 = 62, 62 − 14 = 48, 48 ÷ 3 = 16, 16 x 5 = 80, 80 x 1.25 = 100, 14% of 100 = 14

Intermediate:
501 − 180 = 321, 321 ÷ 3 x 2 = 214, 214 x 2 = 428, 428 ÷ 4 x 3 + 428 = 749, 749 − 627 = 122, 122 + 178 = 300, 22% of 300 = 66

Advanced:
62 x 9 = 558, 558 ÷ 18 x 15 = 465, 465 ÷ 15 x 8 = 248, 248 ÷ 8 x 5 = 155, 155 ÷ 5 x 4 + 155 = 279, 279 ÷ 9 x 2 + 279 = 341, 341 − 192 = 149

113

7	+	3	x	1	−	8	=	2
−		x		+		−		
1	x	8	−	3	+	7	=	12
+		+		x		x		
3	x	7	−	8	+	1	=	14
x		−		−		+		
8	−	1	x	7	+	3	=	52
=		=		=		=		
72		30		25		4		

114

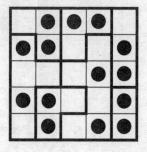

115

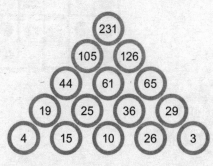

277

116

8	−	3	x	6	=	30
+		x		−		
5	+	7	−	4	=	8
x		−		x		
2	+	1	x	9	=	27
=		=		=		
26		20		18		

117

Beginner:
165 ÷ 3 = 55, 55 + 11 = 66, 66 ÷ 6 = 11, 11² = 121, 121 − 16 = 105, 105 ÷ 21 = 5, 5 + 62 = 67
Intermediate:
48 + 159 = 207, 207 ÷ 9 x 2 = 46, 46 x 2 = 92, 92 − 12 = 80, 25% of 80 = 20, 20² = 400, 75% of 400 = 300
Advanced:
576 x 0.75 = 432, 432 + 64 = 496, 496 + 4 = 500, 71% of 500 = 355, 355 − 15 = 340, 340 ÷ 17 x 3 = 60, 60 ÷ 12 x 7 = 35

118

2	+	9	x	6	−	5	=	61
x		−		+		+		
5	−	2	+	9	x	6	=	72
−		x		x		−		
9	−	6	x	5	+	2	=	17
+		+		−		x		
6	x	5	−	2	+	9	=	37
=		=		=		=		
7		47		73		81		

119

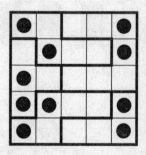

120

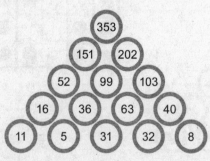

278

121

6	x	5	−	2	=	28
+		−		x		
4	−	1	x	9	=	27
x		x		+		
8	+	3	−	7	=	4
=		=		=		
80		12		25		

122

Beginner:
94 + 6 = 100, square root of 100 = 10, 10 + 25 = 35, 35 ÷ 7 = 5, 5² = 25, 25 x 7 = 175, 175 + 13 = 188

Intermediate:
12.5% of 64 = 8, 8 x 21 = 168, 168 ÷ 3 x 2 = 112, 75% of 112 = 84, 84 ÷ 7 = 12, 12 x 13 = 156, 156 ÷ 6 x 5 = 130

Advanced:
476 ÷ 28 = 17, 17² = 289, 289 x 3 = 867, 867 − 292 = 575, 575 ÷ 23 x 19 = 475, 475 ÷ 0.76 = 625, 625 ÷ 125 = 5

123

9	−	1	+	7	x	2	=	30
+		x		+		+		
2	+	7	−	1	x	9	=	72
x		+		−		x		
7	x	9	+	2	−	1	=	64
−		−		x		−		
1	+	2	x	9	−	7	=	20
=		=		=		=		
76		14		54		4		

124

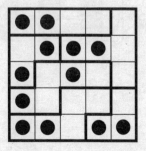

125

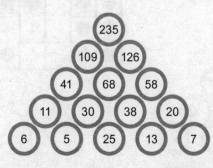

126

9	+	6	x	3	=	45
−		x		+		
5	x	2	−	7	=	3
+		−		x		
8	−	1	x	4	=	28
=		=		=		
12		11		40		

127

Beginner:
57 x 2 = 114, 114 ÷ 3 = 38, 38 + 11 = 49, square root of 49 = 7, 7 x 9 = 63, 63 − 8 = 55, 55 + 17 = 72

Intermediate:
99 x 8 = 792, 792 ÷ 18 = 44, 44 ÷ 11 x 5 = 20, 20^2 = 400, 400 + 41 = 441, square root of 441 = 21, 21 ÷ 7 x 4 = 12

Advanced:
3 to the power of 4 = 81, 81 x 5 = 405, 405 x 1 + 405 ÷ 3 x 2 = 675, 675 x 1 + 675 ÷ 9 x 5 = 1050, 1050 + 39 = 1089, square root of 1089 = 33, 33 x 15 = 495

128

7	−	4	+	5	x	9	=	72
+		x		−		+		
5	x	9	−	4	+	7	=	48
x		−		x		−		
4	+	7	x	9	−	5	=	94
−		+		+		x		
9	−	5	x	7	+	4	=	32
=		=		=		=		
39		34		16		44		

129

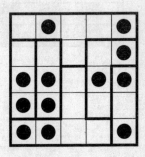

130

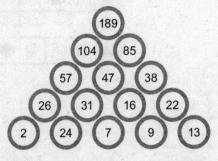

131

3	x	2	+	8	=	14
+		x		−		
5	+	9	−	6	=	8
x		+		+		
7	−	4	+	1	=	4
=		=		=		
56		22		3		

132

Beginner:
Square root of 9 = 3, 3 x 14 = 42, 42 + 6 = 48, 48 ÷ 4 = 12, 12^2 = 144, 144 ÷ 9 = 16, 16 x 3 = 48

Intermediate:
89 + 57 = 146, 146 − 29 = 117, 117 ÷ 9 x 5 = 65, 65 ÷ 5 x 4 = 52, 52 x 7 = 364, 364 x .75 = 273, 273 ÷ 3 = 91

Advanced:
884 ÷ 17 x 3 = 156, 156 + 395 = 551, 551 ÷ 19 x 3 = 87, 87 x 1 + 87 ÷ 3 x 2 = 145, 145 ÷ 29 x 5 = 25, 25 + 44 = 69, 69 ÷ 23 x 14 = 42

133

9	−	6	+	3	x	7	=	42
+		x		+		−		
3	x	7	+	9	−	6	=	24
x		+		x		x		
6	−	3	x	7	+	9	=	30
−		−		−		+		
7	+	9	x	6	−	3	=	93
=		=		=		=		
65		36		78		12		

134

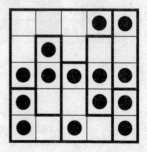

135

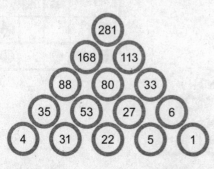

136

2	x	7	–	4	=	10
+		+		x		
5	+	9	–	6	=	8
x		–		+		
1	x	3	+	8	=	11
=		=		=		
7		13		32		

137

Beginner:
329 – 4 = 325, 325 ÷ 5 = 65, 65 x 2 = 130, 130 + 10 = 140, 140 ÷ 20 = 7, 7 – 3 = 4, square root of 4 = 2

Intermediate:
563 + 298 = 861, 861 ÷ 3 x 2 = 574, 50% of 574 = 287, 287 – 125 = 162, 162 x 3 = 486, 486 ÷ 18 = 27, cube root of 27 = 3

Advanced:
729 ÷ 9 x 3 = 243, 243 x 3 = 729, square root of 729 = 27, 27 + 773 = 800, 78% of 800 = 624, 624 ÷ 6 x 5 = 520, 62.5% of 520 = 325

138

5	x	8	–	7	+	9	=	42
+		+		–		x		
8	+	9	x	5	–	7	=	78
x		–		x		+		
7	x	5	–	9	+	8	=	34
–		x		+		–		
9	–	7	x	8	+	5	=	21
=		=		=		=		
82		84		26		66		

139

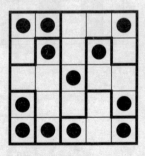

140

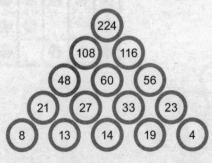

282

141

6	+	4	x	1	=	10
−		+		x		
2	x	9	−	7	=	11
x		x		+		
8	−	3	x	5	=	25
=		=		=		
32		39		12		

142

Beginner:
87 ÷ 3 = 29, 29 + 7 = 36, square root of 36 = 6, 6 x 9 = 54, 54 − 16 = 38, 38 ÷ 2 = 19, 19 + 15 = 34

Intermediate:
42 + 19 = 61, 61 x 9 = 549, 549 ÷ 3 x 2 = 366, 366 ÷ 3 = 122, 122 + 11 = 133, 133 ÷ 7 x 4 = 76, 76 x 4 = 304

Advanced:
997 x 3 = 2991, 2991 + 509 = 3500, 32% of 3500 = 1120, 60% of 1120 = 672, 672 ÷ 3 x 2 = 448, 448 ÷ 16 x 5 = 140, 140 x 1.75 = 245

143

4	+	8	−	1	x	7	=	77
−		+		+		x		
1	x	7	−	4	+	8	=	11
x		x		x		+		
7	+	4	x	8	−	1	=	87
+		−		−		−		
8	−	1	+	7	x	4	=	56
=		=		=		=		
29		59		33		53		

144

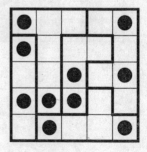

145

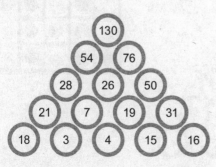

146

2	+	8	x	6	=	60
x		−		+		
5	x	1	+	4	=	9
−		x		x		
9	−	3	x	7	=	42
=		=		=		
1		21		70		

147

Beginner:
$84 \div 7 = 12$, $12^2 = 144$, $144 \div 9 = 16$, square root of 16 = 4, $4 \times 13 = 52$, $52 \div 2 = 26$, $26 + 45 = 71$

Intermediate:
$942 \div 3 = 314$, $314 + 6 = 320$, $320 \div 8 \times 3 = 120$, $120 \div 5 \times 2 = 48$, $48 \div 6 = 8$, $8 \times 1.75 = 14$, $14^2 = 196$

Advanced:
7 to the power of 4 = 2401, $2401 − 701 = 1700$, 29% of $1700 = 493$, $493 \times 2 = 986$, $986 + 292 = 1278$, $1278 \div 18 \times 7 = 497$, $497 − 147 = 350$

148

2	+	9	−	4	x	7	=	49
x		−		+		x		
7	−	4	+	9	x	2	=	24
−		x		−		−		
4	x	7	−	2	+	9	=	35
+		+		x		+		
9	−	2	x	7	+	4	=	53
=		=		=		=		
19		37		77		9		

149

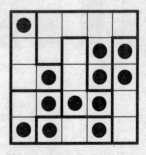

150

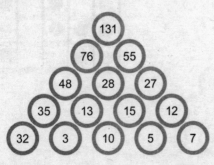

131
76 55
48 28 27
35 13 15 12
32 3 10 5 7

284

151

4	+	8	x	1	=	12
–		x		+		
2	x	5	–	3	=	7
x		–		x		
9	–	7	+	6	=	8
=		=		=		
18		33		24		

152

Beginner:
76 – 4 = 72, 72 ÷ 8 = 9, 9^2 = 81, 81 + 39 = 120, 120 ÷ 3 = 40, 40 – 4 = 36, 36 ÷ 4 = 9

Intermediate:
16^2 = 256, 256 + 429 = 685, 685 ÷ 5 x 4 = 548, 50% of 548 = 274, 274 x 3 = 822, 822 + 36 = 858, 858 – 377 = 481

Advanced:
15 x 75 = 1125, 1125 ÷ 3 x 2 = 750, 750 ÷ 25 = 30, 30 x 2.6 = 78, 78 + 78 ÷ 3 = 104, 37.5% of 104 = 39, 39 x 1 2/3 = 65

153

5	+	9	x	6	–	8	=	76
+		–		x		+		
6	–	5	x	8	+	9	=	17
–		x		+		–		
9	–	8	+	5	x	6	=	36
x		+		–		x		
8	+	6	–	9	x	5	=	25
=		=		=		=		
16		38		44		55		

154

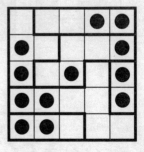

155

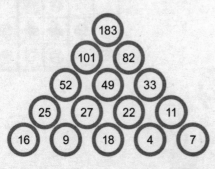

285

156

5	−	1	x	3	=	12
+		x		+		
8	x	6	−	7	=	41
x		−		x		
4	−	2	x	9	=	18
=		=		=		
52		4		90		

157

Beginner:
$36 ÷ 3 = 12$, $12 − 4 = 8$, $8^2 = 64$, $64 \times 2 = 128$, $128 ÷ 4 = 32$, $32 ÷ 2 = 16$, $16 − 11 = 5$

Intermediate:
$51 ÷ 3 = 17$, $17 + 93 = 110$, $110 ÷ 10 \times 3 = 33$, $33 ÷ 11 = 3$, $3^3 = 27$, $27 \times 2 = 54$, $54 ÷ 9 \times 4 = 24$

Advanced:
$1017 ÷ 3 = 339$, $339 ÷ 3 \times 2 = 226$, $226 + 124 = 350$, $350 \times 0.38 = 133$, $133 + 77 = 210$, $210 ÷ 14 \times 5 = 75$, $75 + 45 = 120$

158

7	−	1	+	3	x	6	=	54
+		+		x		−		
3	+	6	x	7	−	1	=	62
x		x		−		+		
1	x	7	+	6	−	3	=	10
−		−		+		x		
6	−	3	+	1	x	7	=	28
=		=		=		=		
4		46		16		56		

159

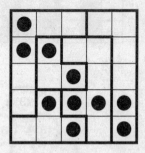

160

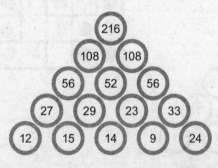

216

108 — 108

56 — 52 — 56

27 — 29 — 23 — 33

12 — 15 — 14 — 9 — 24

161

5	+	9	−	4	=	10
−		+		x		
2	x	7	+	1	=	15
x		x		+		
3	+	6	x	8	=	72
=		=		=		
9		96		12		

162

Beginner:
13^2 = 169, 169 + 31 = 200, 200 ÷ 4 = 50, 50 x 5 = 250, 250 + 25 = 275, 275 − 125 = 150, 150 ÷ 3 = 50

Intermediate:
21 ÷ 7 x 2 = 6, 6 + 15 = 21, 21^2 = 441, 441 ÷ 9 x 2 = 98, 98 + 4 = 102, 102 ÷ 17 = 6, 6^3 = 216

Advanced:
87.5% of 720 = 630, 630 ÷ 18 x 7 = 245, 245 x 2 = 490, 490 ÷ 14 x 9 = 315, 180% of 315 = 567, 567 ÷ 3 = 189, 189 ÷ 9 x 5 + 189 = 294

163

7	+	9	−	2	x	3	=	42
−		−		+		x		
2	x	7	−	3	+	9	=	20
x		+		x		−		
9	−	3	x	7	+	2	=	44
+		x		−		+		
3	+	2	x	9	−	7	=	38
=		=		=		=		
48		10		26		32		

164

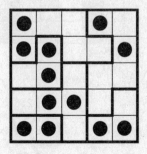

165

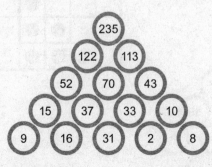

287

166

3	+	2	x	6	=	30
−		x		+		
1	x	8	−	5	=	3
x		+		x		
9	−	4	x	7	=	35
=		=		=		
18		20		77		

167

Beginner:
59 − 26 = 33, 33 ÷ 11 = 3, 3 x 7 = 21, 21 + 14 = 35, 35 + 7 = 42, 42 ÷ 6 = 7, 7 x 4 = 28

Intermediate:
221 ÷ 13 = 17, 17 x 4 = 68, 68 ÷ 4 x 3 = 51, 51 ÷ 3 = 17, 17 + 64 = 81, square root of 81 = 9, 9 x 14 = 126

Advanced:
203 ÷ 29 x 5 = 35, 120% of 35 = 42, 42 ÷ 7 x 3 = 18, 18^2 = 324, 324 + 276 = 600, 32% of 600 = 192, 192 ÷ 3 x 2 + 192 = 320

168

3	+	9	−	7	x	5	=	25
x		−		+		−		
7	−	5	x	9	+	3	=	21
−		x		x		+		
9	−	3	x	5	+	7	=	37
+		+		−		x		
5	x	7	+	3	−	9	=	29
=		=		=		=		
17		19		77		81		

169

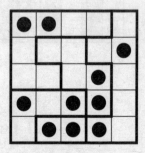

170

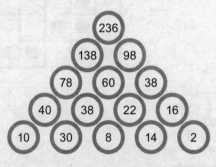

171

9	−	1	+	6	=	14
−		+		x		
5	x	3	−	8	=	7
x		x		−		
7	+	2	x	4	=	36
=		=		=		
28		2		44		

172

Beginner:
75 x 7 = 525, 525 ÷ 25 = 21, 21 ÷ 7 = 3, 3 x 16 = 48, 48 ÷ 6 = 8, 8 ÷ 4 = 2, 2 x 98 = 196
Intermediate:
7^3 = 343, 343 + 7 = 350, 350 + 35 = 385, 385 x 0.4 = 154, 154 x 2 = 308, 308 x 0.75 = 231, 231 + 169 = 400
Advanced:
67 + 28 = 95, 95 ÷ 19 x 8 = 40, 90% of 40 = 36, 36 + 6 = 42, 900% of 42 = 378, 378 ÷ 18 x 7 = 147, 147 + (147 ÷ 3 x 2) = 245

173

4	x	6	−	8	+	5	=	21
+		−		−		x		
8	−	5	x	4	+	6	=	18
−		x		x		−		
6	+	8	−	5	x	4	=	36
x		+		+		+		
5	−	4	x	6	+	8	=	14
=		=		=		=		
30		12		26		34		

174

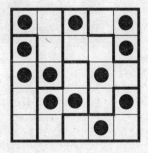

175

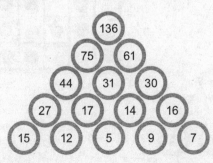

289

176

5	+	6	x	4	=	44
−		+		x		
2	x	9	−	3	=	15
x		−		+		
7	−	1	x	8	=	48
=		=		=		
21		14		20		

177

Beginner:
87 + 9 = 96, 96 ÷ 12 = 8, 8 + 12 = 20, 20 + 1 = 21, 21 ÷ 7 = 3, 3 x 19 = 57, 57 + 73 = 130
Intermediate:
225 ÷ 9 x 2 = 50, 50^2 = 2500, 2500 + 250 = 2750, 2750 ÷ 25 = 110, 110 ÷ 5 = 22, 22 x 12 = 264, 264 ÷ 3 x 2 = 176
Advanced:
149 x 5 = 745, 40% of 745 = 298, 298 + 2 = 300, 58% of 300 = 174, (174 ÷ 3) + 174 = 232, 232 ÷ 8 x 5 = 145, 145 ÷ 5 x 4 = 116

178

5	+	8	−	1	x	6	=	72
−		x		+		x		
1	x	5	+	6	−	8	=	3
x		−		x		−		
8	−	6	x	5	+	1	=	11
+		+		−		+		
6	−	1	+	8	x	5	=	65
=		=		=		=		
38		35		27		52		

179

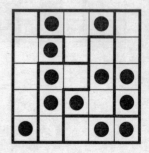

180

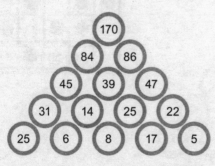

290

181

9	x	3	–	5	=	22
–		+		x		
6	–	2	x	7	=	28
x		x		–		
1	+	8	–	4	=	5
=		=		=		
3		40		31		

182

Beginner:
48 ÷ 4 = 12, 12 + 114 = 126, 126 ÷ 6 = 21, 21 – 15 = 6, 6 + 7 = 13, 13^2 = 169, 169 + 31 = 200
Intermediate:
61 – 15 = 46, 46 x 3 = 138, 138 x 1.5 = 207, 207 ÷ 9 = 23, 23 + 57 = 80, 80 ÷ 10 x 7 = 56, 56 x 11 = 616
Advanced:
15^2 = 225, 225 x 4 = 900, 33% of 900 = 297, 297 ÷ 9 x 5 = 165, 60% of 165 = 99, 99 x 8 = 792, 792 ÷ 0.2 = 3960

183

3	x	7	+	9	–	8	=	22
+		–		–		+		
8	–	3	x	7	+	9	=	44
x		x		+		–		
9	–	8	+	3	x	7	=	28
–		+		x		x		
7	+	9	–	8	x	3	=	24
=		=		=		=		
92		41		40		30		

184

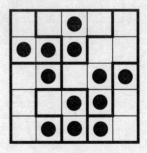

185

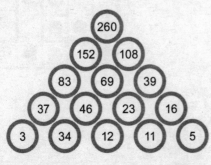

291

186

4	x	9	–	1	=	35
+		–		x		
7	–	2	x	6	=	30
x		+		–		
5	+	8	–	3	=	10
=		=		=		
55		15		3		

187

Beginner:
6 x 13 = 78, 78 ÷ 3 = 26, 26 + 78 = 104, 104 x 2 = 208, 208 ÷ 4 = 52, 52 – 18 = 34, 34 ÷ 2 = 17

Intermediate:
543 x 1 1/3 = 724, 724 ÷ 2 = 362, 362 – 106 = 256, square root of 256 = 16, 16 x 1.25 = 20, 20 ÷ 0.5 = 40, 40 ÷ 8 x 5 = 25

Advanced:
572 ÷ 11 x 7 = 364, 364 ÷ 52 x 9 = 63, 63 ÷ 9 x 5 = 35, 35² = 1225, 60% of 1225 = 735, 735 ÷ 15 x 4 = 196, square root of 196 = 14

188

4	+	8	–	2	x	6	=	60
x		–		+		x		
2	x	6	+	4	–	8	=	8
+		+		x		–		
8	–	2	+	6	x	4	=	48
–		x		–		+		
6	+	4	x	8	–	2	=	78
=		=		=		=		
10		16		28		46		

189

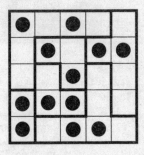

190

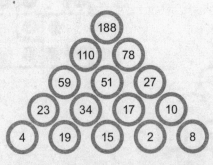

188
110 · 78
59 · 51 · 27
23 · 34 · 17 · 10
4 · 19 · 15 · 2 · 8

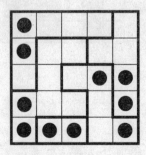

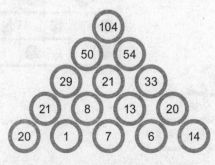

191

3	x	1	+	7	=	10
+		x		−		
6	+	8	x	5	=	70
x		−		x		
4	−	2	+	9	=	11
=		=		=		
36		6		18		

192

Beginner:
187 − 16 = 171, 171 ÷ 9 = 19,
19 − 4 = 15, 15² = 225, 225 ÷
25 = 9, 9 + 5 = 14, 14 + 73 = 87
Intermediate:
269 + 47 = 316, 316 ÷ 4 = 79,
79 x 3 = 237, 237 − 88 = 149,
149 + 27 = 176, 176 ÷ 8 x 5 =
110, 110 + 11 = 121
Advanced:
631 x 5 = 3155, 3155 + 60% =
5048, 5048 ÷ 2 = 2524, 2524
x 3.75 = 9465, 9465 ÷ 15 x 6 =
3786, 3786 + 214 = 4000, 73%
of 4000 = 2920

193

4	+	7	−	8	x	3	=	9
x		−		−		+		
8	−	3	x	4	+	7	=	27
−		x		+		x		
7	x	8	−	3	+	4	=	57
+		+		x		−		
3	+	4	x	7	−	8	=	41
=		=		=		=		
28		36		49		32		

195

194

196

1	x	9	+	5	=	14
x		−		+		
4	−	3	x	7	=	7
+		x		x		
6	+	8	−	2	=	12
=		=		=		
10		48		24		

197

Beginner:
111 ÷ 3 = 37, 37 − 12 = 25, square root of 25 = 5, 5 x 15 = 75, 75 + 105 = 180, 5% of 180 = 9, square root of 9 = 3

Intermediate:
414 ÷ 9 x 5 = 230, 230 x 0.9 = 207, 207 x 5 = 1035, 1035 ÷ 3 x 2 = 690, 690 + 230 = 920, 920 ÷ 20 = 46, 46 x 3 = 138

Advanced:
38 x 22 = 836, 836 − 212 = 624, 624 ÷ 12 x 9 = 468, 468 ÷ 6 = 78, 350% of 78 = 273, 273 ÷ 13 x 5 = 105, 105 ÷ 21 x 5 = 25

198

5	x	3	−	9	+	6	=	12
−		+		x		x		
3	x	6	+	5	−	9	=	14
x		−		−		−		
9	−	5	x	6	+	3	=	27
+		x		+		+		
6	+	9	x	3	−	5	=	40
=		=		=		=		
24		36		42		56		

199

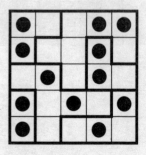

200

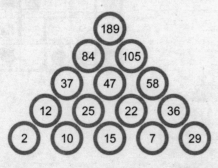

294

201

5	+	8	–	1	=	12
x		–		+		
3	x	7	+	9	=	30
+		x		x		
6	–	2	x	4	=	16
=		=		=		
21		2		40		

202

Beginner:
235 ÷ 5 = 47, 47 x 2 = 94, 94 – 19 = 75, 75 x 9 = 675, 675 + 215 = 890, 890 + 89 = 979, 979 – 190 = 789
Intermediate:
47 x 3 = 141, 141 – 75 = 66, 66 x 2 = 132, 132 ÷ 6 x 5 = 110, 110 x 0.8 = 88, 88 ÷ 4 x 3 = 66, 66 x 4 = 264
Advanced:
22^2 = 484, 484 x 1.25 = 605, 40% of 605 = 242, 242 + 254 = 496, 496 x .375 = 186, (186 ÷ 3) + 186 = 248, 248 ÷ 8 x 5 = 155

203

9	–	1	+	8	x	6	=	96
x		+		–		x		
6	+	8	x	1	–	9	=	5
–		–		x		–		
8	–	6	x	9	+	1	=	19
+		x		+		+		
1	x	9	–	6	+	8	=	11
=		=		=		=		
47		27		69		61		

204

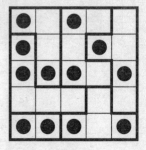

205

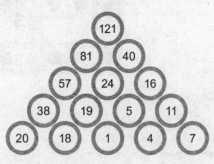

206

5	x	7	–	2	=	33
–		+		x		
4	+	9	–	6	=	7
x		x		+		
8	–	1	x	3	=	21
=		=		=		
8		16		15		

207

Beginner:
$10^2 = 100$, $100 – 14 = 86$, $86 ÷ 2 = 43$, $43 + 17 = 60$, 20% of 60 = 12, $12^2 = 144$, $144 + 56 = 200$

Intermediate:
$120 ÷ 15 × 2 = 16$, $16 × 4 = 64$, $64 × 2 = 128$, $128 ÷ 8 × 5 = 80$, $80 × 1.3 = 104$, $104 ÷ 4 = 26$, $26 × 7 = 182$

Advanced:
$14^2 = 196$, $196 × 2 = 392$, $392 ÷ 8 × 3 = 147$, $147 ÷ 49 × 5 = 15$, $15 × 12 = 180$, $180 × 0.45 = 81$, square root of 81 = 9

208

7	–	1	+	6	x	8	=	96
x		+		x		–		
8	+	6	x	7	–	1	=	97
–		x		+		x		
6	x	8	–	1	+	7	=	54
+		–		–		+		
1	x	7	+	8	–	6	=	9
=		=		=		=		
51		49		35		55		

209

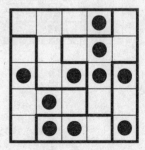

210

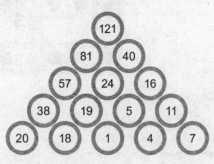

6	–	4	x	8	=	16
x		+		–		
1	+	7	x	5	=	40
+		x		+		
9	x	3	–	2	=	25
=		=		=		
15		33		5		

212

Beginner:
$61 + 5 = 66$, $66 \div 11 = 6$, $6 \times 13 = 78$, $78 \div 3 \times 2 = 52$, $52 \div 2 = 26$, $26 – 8 = 18$, $18 \times 3 = 54$

Intermediate:
$329 – 24 = 305$, $305 \div 5 = 61$, $61 + 99 = 160$, $160 \div 5 \times 4 = 128$, $128 \times 3 = 384$, $384 \div 6 \times 5 = 320$, $320 \div 16 = 20$

Advanced:
$228 \div 12 \times 9 = 171$, $171 \div 9 \times 5 = 95$, $95 \div 19 \times 6 = 30$, $30^2 = 900$, 27% of $900 = 243$, $243 \times 2 = 486$, $486 \div 27 \times 5 = 90$

213

6	+	3	–	8	x	2	=	2
x		+		–		x		
3	x	8	+	2	–	6	=	20
–		x		x		+		
8	–	2	+	6	x	3	=	36
+		–		+		–		
2	+	6	–	3	x	8	=	40
=		=		=		=		
12		16		39		7		

214

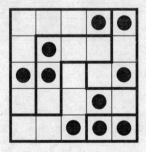

215

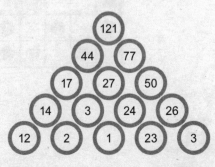

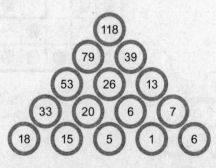
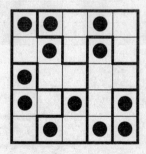

216

5	x	1	+	3	=	8
+		x		+		
9	–	6	x	8	=	24
x		–		x		
2	+	4	x	7	=	42
=		=		=		
28		2		77		

217

Beginner:
476 ÷ 2 = 238, 238 + 32 = 270, 270 ÷ 3 = 90, 40% of 90 = 36, square root of 36 = 6, 6 + 15 = 21, 21 ÷ 7 = 3
Intermediate:
1973 – 982 = 991, 991 + 39 = 1030, 1030 + 148 = 1178, 1178 ÷ 19 = 62, 62 x 7 = 434, 434 – 48 = 386, 386 ÷ 2 = 193
Advanced:
24^2 = 576, 576 ÷ 12 x 3 = 144, square root of 144 = 12, 12 x 1.25 = 15, 15 x 25 = 375, 375 ÷ 15 x 4 = 100, 100 ÷ 0.4 = 250

218

3	+	5	x	4	–	9	=	23
+		–		x		–		
9	–	4	x	5	+	3	=	28
–		x		–		x		
4	x	9	–	3	+	5	=	38
x		+		+		+		
5	–	3	x	9	+	4	=	22
=		=		=		=		
40		12		26		34		

219

220

221

6	+	8	−	3	=	11
x		+		x		
7	−	2	x	5	=	25
−		x		+		
4	x	9	−	1	=	35
=		=		=		
38		90		16		

222

Beginner:
522 ÷ 9 = 58, 58 + 12 = 70, 10% of 70 = 7, 7 x 5 = 35, 35 + 45 = 80, 80 x 1.05 = 84, 84 ÷ 12 = 7

Intermediate:
41 + 92 = 133, 133 x 4 = 532, 532 ÷ 4 x 3 = 399, 399 + 266 = 665, 665 + 85 = 750, 750 x 1.3 = 975, 975 − 489 = 486

Advanced:
38 x 16 = 608, 608 ÷ 8 x 3 = 228, 228 ÷ 19 x 5 = 60, 60 + 45% = 87, 87 + 58 = 145, 145 ÷ 29 x 27 = 135, 135 ÷ 15 x 11 = 99

223

7	+	9	−	4	x	8	=	96
x		−		+		−		
8	−	4	x	9	+	7	=	43
+		x		−		+		
4	x	8	−	7	+	9	=	34
−		+		x		x		
9	−	7	x	8	+	4	=	20
=		=		=		=		
51		47		48		40		

224

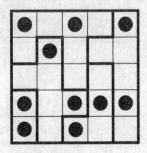

225

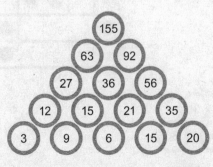

226

6	–	1	x	5	=	25
+		+		x		
2	x	4	+	8	=	16
x		x		–		
7	+	9	x	3	=	48
=		=		=		
56		45		37		

227

Beginner:
15 ÷ 3 x 2 = 10, 10 + 20% = 12, 12 x 14 = 168, 168 ÷ 3 = 56, 56 – 27 = 29, 29 x 2 = 58, 58 + 142 = 200

Intermediate:
127 x 3 = 381, 381 + 69 = 450, 450 x 1.2 = 540, 540 ÷ 9 x 7 = 420, 420 + 21 = 441, square root of 441 = 21, 21 ÷ 7 x 2 + 21 = 27

Advanced:
44 ÷ 11 x 7 = 28, 28 ÷ 7 x 5 = 20, 20 + 60% = 32, 32^2 = 1024, 1024 ÷ 16 x 5 = 320, 320 ÷ 20 x 5 = 80, 80 ÷ 1.25 = 64

228

6	–	1	+	7	x	4	=	48
–		x		+		+		
4	x	7	–	1	+	6	=	33
x		–		x		x		
7	–	4	x	6	+	1	=	19
+		+		–		–		
1	+	6	–	4	x	7	=	21
=		=		=		=		
15		9		44		3		

229

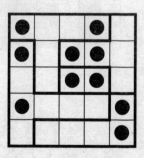

230

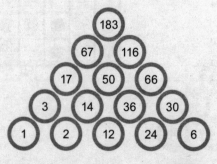

300

231

6	+	9	x	2	=	30
–		–		x		
4	x	7	–	5	=	23
x		x		+		
1	x	3	+	8	=	11
=		=		=		
2		6		18		

232

Beginner:
50% of 250 = 125, 125 ÷ 5 = 25, 25 x 7 = 175, 175 x 2 = 350, 350 + 40 = 390, 390 x 1.2 = 468, 468 ÷ 9 = 52

Intermediate:
49 ÷ 7 x 6 = 42, 42 ÷ 3 = 14, 14 x 5 = 70, 70 ÷ 0.2 = 350, 350 ÷ 5 x 4 = 280, 280 ÷ 70 = 4, 4^3 = 64

Advanced:
24 ÷ 0.25 = 96, 96 ÷ 12 x 7 = 56, 56 x 1.875 = 105, 105 ÷ 21 x 19 = 95, 95 ÷ 19 x 7 = 35, 35 ÷ 7 x 5 + 35 = 60, 60 ÷ 1.25 = 48

233

5	+	9	–	8	x	2	=	12
–		+		+		x		
2	x	8	–	5	+	9	=	20
x		x		x		–		
9	–	5	+	2	x	8	=	48
+		–		–		+		
8	–	2	x	9	+	5	=	59
=		=		=		=		
35		83		17		15		

234

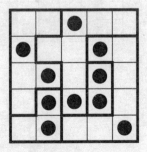

235

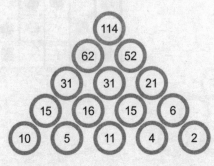

236

9	−	5	x	1	=	4
−		x		+		
3	x	8	+	6	=	30
x		−		x		
7	−	2	x	4	=	20
=		=		=		
42		38		28		

237

Beginner:
Square root of 169 = 13, 13 x 4 = 52, 52 + 15 = 67, 67 − 27 = 40, 15% of 40 = 6, 6 + 17 = 23, 23 x 8 = 184

Intermediate:
396 + 264 = 660, 660 ÷ 11 x 4 = 240, 240 ÷ 12 x 5 = 100, 100 x 0.33 = 33, 33 x 9 = 297, 297 x 2 = 594, 594 ÷ 18 x 5 = 165

Advanced:
65 ÷ 13 x 7 = 35, 60% of 35 = 21, 21^2 = 441, 441 ÷ 9 x 4 = 196, 196 x 1.25 = 245, 40% of 245 = 98, 98 x 7 = 686

238

4	+	8	−	3	x	5	=	45
x		−		+		−		
5	−	4	x	8	+	3	=	11
−		x		x		+		
3	x	5	−	4	+	8	=	19
+		+		−		x		
8	−	3	x	5	+	4	=	29
=		=		=		=		
25		23		39		40		

239

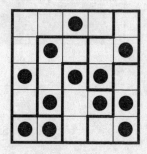

240

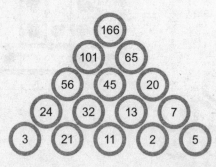

241

3	+	7	x	5	=	50
+		+		+		
1	x	4	+	9	=	13
x		x		x		
6	+	8	–	2	=	12
=		=		=		
24		88		28		

242

Beginner:
196 ÷ 4 = 49, square root of 49 = 7, 7 + 28 = 35, 35 x 3 = 105, 105 + 29 = 134, 134 ÷ 2 = 67, 67 + 27 = 94

Intermediate:
39 x 5 = 195, 195 ÷ 3 x 2 = 130, 130 x 1.6 = 208, 208 ÷ 4 x 3 = 156, 156 + 92 = 248, 248 x 3 = 744, 744 + 146 = 890

Advanced:
72 x 18 = 1296, 1296 ÷ 8 x 3 = 486, 486 ÷ 18 x 7 = 189, 189 + 83 = 272, 272 ÷ 17 x 14 = 224, 12.5% of 224 = 28, 28 ÷ 0.2 = 140

243

8	–	4	+	7	x	5	=	55
–		x		–		+		
5	+	7	x	4	–	8	=	40
x		–		x		–		
7	x	5	+	8	–	4	=	39
+		+		+		x		
4	+	8	–	5	x	7	=	49
=		=		=		=		
25		31		29		63		

244

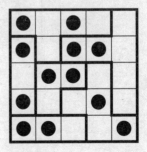

245

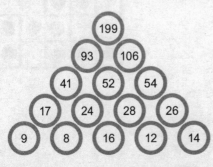

303

246

4	+	8	−	6	=	6
x		−		+		
1	x	5	+	3	=	8
+		x		−		
9	−	7	x	2	=	4
=		=		=		
13		21		7		

247

Beginner:
Cube root of 125 = 5, 5 x 9 = 45, 45 + 13 = 58, 58 ÷ 2 = 29, 29 + 52 = 81, square root of 81 = 9, 9 ÷ 3 x 2 = 6

Intermediate:
17^2 = 289, 289 x 2 = 578, 578 + 125 = 703, 703 x 3 = 2109, 2109 − 1617 = 492, 492 + 164 = 656, 656 − 497 = 159

Advanced:
89 x 3 = 267, 267 ÷ 0.3 = 890, 890 + 60% = 1424, 1424 ÷ 8 x 3 = 534, 534 + 266 = 800, 19% of 800 = 152, 152 ÷ 19 x 5 = 40

248

9	−	2	+	4	x	3	=	33
+		x		+		−		
3	+	4	x	9	−	2	=	61
x		+		x		+		
2	x	9	−	3	+	4	=	19
−		−		−		x		
4	−	3	+	2	x	9	=	27
=		=		=		=		
20		14		37		45		

249

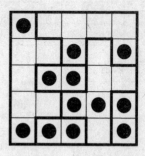